S. PARRIS

Comments on Parkinson's: a patient's view

"I was enthralled and stimulated to read how one man and his family faced up to the challenges set by Parkinson's disease."
Mary G Baker MBE, National and International Development Consultant, Parkinson's Disease Society

"When I first read this book, it was like meeting a friend with lots of similar ideas about coping with Parkinson's. Mine came from listening to hundreds of people with Parkinson's; Sidney's were distilled from his own unique experiences as a patient. I am delighted that many more people will now have the chance to learn from his experience."
Marie Oxtoby, co-author of **Parkinson's at your fingertips**

"Many patients will benefit from reading this remarkable book and may it encourage them to believe that their own views will be heard."
Adrian Williams, co-author of **Parkinson's at your fingertips**

"Accommodation without surrender is the theme of this book as it was of Sid's life. He must have been the most experienced and well informed of all Parkinsonians (and their doctors!). His enthusiasm for his subject was tempered by a common sense approach. This book will encourage all sufferers to follow his example by becoming well informed, always enquiring and never giving in to the symptoms of this unpredictable, mysterious and sometimes bizarre condition."
John Coop, a British friend of Sidney Dorros's

"By looking at Parkinson's disease from the angle of the patient, Sidney Dorros was ahead of his time. He invested his courage with the hard graft of his personal effort and succeeded in forming groups of Parkinson's sufferers and their families into an influential force which mobilised the medical establishment to focus on all aspects of the illness. This British edition is a lasting tribute to his staying power and his inspirational effort to overcome the disease and help others with his experience and his dynamic approach."
Cecil Todes MRCP, FRCPsych, author of **Shadow over my brain – a battle against Parkinson's Disease**

Comments on **Parkinson's at your fingertips** by *Professor Adrian Williams and Dr Marie Oxtoby, also published by Class Publishing. (Please see the back of the book for further details about this book.)*

"This book deserves to be an unqualified success."
Dr Andrew Lees, Consultant Neurologist, The National Hospital for Neurology and Neurosurgery, London

"... provides the answers to so many questions..."
Mary G Baker MBE, National and International Development Consultant, Parkinson's Disease Society

"In my opinion this book strikes a perfect balance between information and sympathy, without being too technical or too maudlin. I feel sure that this book will become a vade mecum for anyone associated with Parkinson's, whether it be the patient, carer, GP or therapist. I feel sure that it will fill a very much needed gap in the market for educating and reassuring all those who are involved in any way with Parkinson's."
Dr Lloyd A Frost, Leeds

"I found the book easy to read and comprehensive. Patients and carers must take the information, and demand or even, with the help of others, set about making it happen themselves, if they wish to get the best of what is available. A super DIY manual for patients and carers."
Dr Bernard Dean, Kimbolton

"Congratulations to Marie Oxtoby and Professor Williams for writing the most informative book for people with Parkinson's, their carers, doctors, nurses, and all services involved."
Jane Stewart, Parkinson's Nurse Specialist Project Coordinator

"I think the book is excellent and I am so pleased that the response has been so positive from our members. We at the Parkinson's Disease Society have been very excited about this whole project."
Pauline Smith, Director of Operations, Parkinson's Disease Society

"I think **Parkinson's at your fingertips** is really first class – quite excellent – and I would recommend anyone linked with the disease to have a copy to refer to."
Derek Sangster, Worthing

"Although I have had many years caring for my husband who has Parkinson's disease, and as a result know quite a lot about the illness, I found much helpful information in your book. It is very easy to read and comprehend, and shows a deep understanding for the problems of both the patients and their carers."

Thelma Bennett, Hornby

"I find it very informative; what I have read so far has helped me or will help me allay some of the fear I once had of Parkinson's."

Mrs Rhoda Scott, Chichester

PARKINSON'S
A Patient's View

FIRST BRITISH EDITION

Sidney Dorros

*With an introduction
by Les Essex*

CLASS PUBLISHING • LONDON

First printed in the United States of America
Second printing 1992

First British Edition printed in Great Britain 1998

The publishers welcome feedback from the users of this book
Please contact the publishers.
Class Publishing, Barb House, Barb Mews, London W6 7PA
Telephone: 0171 371 2119
Fax: 0171 371 2878 [International + 44171]
email: post@class.co.uk

A CIP catalogue record for this book is available from the British Library

ISBN 1 872362 70 2

Production by Landmark Production Consultants Ltd, Princes Risborough

Printed and bound by Clays Ltd, St Ives plc

To my mother, members of the Parkinsonian Society of Greater Washington, and other fellow parkinsonians who have served as inspiring examples of how to live with a chronic ailment;

To my family and friends whose daily encouragement and support sustained me emotionally through the eight years it took to complete this work;

To the medical research and health-care personnel whose discoveries and treatment have made it physically possible for many parkinsonians to enjoy a meaninfgul life; and

To my wife, Donna, whose unstinting love and care have sustained me for a decade and inspired many other parkinsonians and their spouses to *"Accommodate Without Surrender."*

Preface

ALTHOUGH PARKINSON'S DISEASE is one of the
most common of the chronic disabling disorders of the
nervous system, relevant literature is almost exclusively
confined to medical and scientific writings about its nature and treatment. Accounts of what it is like to be "on
the receiving end" are rare, and those which have been
written are brief.

With *Parkinson's: A Patient's View*, Sidney Dorros
fulfills the need for an articulate and comprehensive
record of a patient's experiences in parkinsonism and its
treatments. The author has devoted substantial time and
energy describing the experience of having long-term
impairment of motor function—the impact of being
unable to move quickly, of having difficulty in starting to
walk, negotiating a doorway, getting out of a chair; the
problem of uncontrollable tremor; and the frustration of
disabling writhing movements that are a side effect of
treatment. This story tells of the struggle to accept the
uniquely personal information that one has a serious,
permanent illness; of making psychological and physical
adjustments to the limitations imposed by the disease; and
of generating the tenacious determination required to
make life worth living in spite of everything.

Mr. Dorros provides a starkly personal account of
the ways that his life was disrupted by chronic disease. He
is direct in facing facts which have to be faced: from the

public embarrassment of a movement disorder to the private disturbance of his sexual life.

In addition, this book describes the plight of being a subject for clinical observations, which should be of considerable interest to those who conduct clinical research and to those who hold strong views on the ethics of human experimentation. Most of all, however, the book should be read by those who have Parkinson's disease, by their relatives, and by their physicians. By those who have Parkinson's, so that they may know how others have adapted to the illness. By their relatives, so that they may know better how to help their loved ones. By their physicians, so that they may learn the crucial effect that their small, seemingly trivial, signals can have on their ability to establish and maintain the confidence of a patient.

D.B. Calne, D.M., F.R.C.P.
Bethesda, Maryland, USA
June, 1981

Acknowledgements

THE DISABILITIES imposed by parkinsonism caused me to work at a frustratingly slow pace on this book and to put the work aside several times during the past eight years. It would still be set aside were it not for the frequent prodding, the sharing of ideas, and the typing of countless drafts from seemingly illegible scrawls or inaudible dictation by my deceased wife Debbie and, later, by Donna Preudhomme. Their gentle prodding was reinforced by notes, phone calls, and editorial suggestions by former colleague and editor of the NEA *Journal*, Dr. Mildred Fenner Reid; and by the not-so-gentle prodding of friend Bruno Weinschel. Bruno extended my working time on the book by providing specially selected recording equipment that enabled me to dictate even when I was stiff or had uncontrollable movements.

Drs. Thomas Chase, Donald Calne, and Christopher Ward of the National Institute for Neurological and Communicative Disorders and Stroke helped define the kinds of information that would be most useful from a scientific and medical point of view. I am especially grateful to Dr. Calne for his careful final review of the manuscript and for his foreword; and to Dr. Chase for his insightful discussions of the implications of the studies in which I was a subject and for assigning nurse-practitioner Marjorie Gillespie to help sift through the voluminous NIH records of my twelve years as an experimental patient. The records were so complete that we were able to determine how many milligrams of levodopa I got and how I looked and felt after lunch on a given day of a double-blind study.

Robert Hinkle of the information office at NINCDS has been remarkably prompt, gracious, and accurate in tracking down hard-to-find information about parkinsonism during the past decade.

I am indebted to NIH Social Workers Dr. Robert Savard for valuable guidance, and Ruth Kaneshiro for planting the seed that has grown to be the Parkinsonian Society of Greater Washington.

Sandra Meadows has often helped me find a way through the maze to NIH resources and also gave an early version of the manuscript a thorough and valuable copy editing.

Walter Rybeck and Rita and Leon Kosofsky are representative of several friends who shared their writing and editorial skills by providing ideas and criticisms.

Dr. Roger Duvoisin's encouraging comments and suggestions upon reading the manuscript at two different stages helped me focus more sharply on the patient's view of parkinsonism.

I thank the other reviewers of the nearly final manuscript who provided written critiques: Amy Pollard, Harold McConeghey, and Minerva Math. It was Minerva, a fellow parkinsonian and member of PSGW, who conceived the phrase "Accommodation Without Surrender" to summarize my autobiographical account. And Harold McConeghey saw "Make Your Own Miracle" as the message of the book.

Kathleen Roche and Mrs. Irene Southers are two of several nurses and other medical support personnel at NIH whose influence helped me to appreciate the healing powers of love and other positive emotions several years before Norman Cousins wrote about them in *Anatomy of an Illness*. For his exemplary spiritual faith, I am also grateful to friend and neighbor William Boese.

The Sisters of Charity of Kentucky, who have hosted the Parkinsonian Society at Camp Maria for four years, and George Foster, a Catholic lay deacon, initiator of the Camp Maria vacations for Parkinsonians and a key leader of PSGW, have reinforced my appreciation of the importance of the positive emotions without attempting to convert me to their religious faith.

As a former publisher I especially appreciate the creative contributions of Calvin Kytle, president of Seven Locks Press, the unremitting attention to accuracy, clarity, and style by editor Ira Brodsky, and the accommodation of both men to my physical limitations and their patience with my idiosyncrasies.

And finally, I thank my children, Arthur, Ellen, David, and Carol, my son-in-law David Crandall, and other family members who, when I told them I would delete any reference to them in the book that might embarrass or upset them, all said, in one way or another, "If it will help other people, even if it might be embarrassing, tell it like it is."

Sidney Dorros
Gaithersburg, Maryland, USA
July, 1981

Contents

"... the disease ... the man ... the world go together and cannot be considered separately as things in themselves. An adequate concept or characterization of a man ... would embrace all that happened to him, all that affected him, and all that he affected. ..."

Dr Oliver Sacks in *Awakening*

Introduction

BY SIDNEY DORROS

UNTIL RECENTLY, Parkinson's disease, or parkinsonism, was one of the most debilitating disorders of the
nervous system. Today it is possible, with the aid of
advanced medical care and self-help, to alleviate and
adjust to the symptoms sufficiently to live fairly comfor-
tably. But coping with parkinsonism—as a patient, family
member, or medical practitioner—takes much understanding; for it remains one of the most mysterious and
complex of human illnesses. It affects and is affected by
almost every aspect of the lives of its victims and the
people around them.

This book includes a detailed autobiographical account
of how my family and I have coped with parkinsonism for
twenty years. To convey a realistic picture, we have
exposed intimate aspects of our lives that we would prefer
to forget or to keep private. I hope that our candor will
provide new insights to help others deal with the ailment.

Our story may also offer hope and help to people with
any chronic and as yet incurable ailment; *hope* that
medical science will suddenly open a new door for them to
return to life, as it did for me; and *help* in shaping attitudes
and actions conducive to coping with illness and life in
general.

My experiences with parkinsonism have been extensive, varied, and dramatic. I've had the dubious distinc-
tion of contracting the condition at an uncommonly early

age and undergoing all the major treatments of the past two decades. For still unknown reasons, both my mother and father were also stricken with parkinsonism. For each of us the symptoms followed a different course and we responded differently to the ailment and to treatment.

Three times, parkinsonism has reduced me to almost complete incapacitation and abject depression, and three times I've experienced dramatic rescues by modern medicine. The first time was by amazingly delicate and skillful brain surgery, called cryosurgery; then I became the first experimental patient at the National Institute of Health (NIH) upon whom L-Dopa worked its magic; and, when the long-term side effects of L-Dopa threatened to become almost as bad as the illness, I became one of the first experimental patients in the United States to benefit from bromocriptine, a new type of drug for neurological ailments. The latest treatment with bromocriptine has not, at this writing, restored anywhere near normal function, and I remain unable to return to work; but the improvement has been enough to enable me to enjoy life in the present and to look forward to the future with hope. This condition contrasts sharply with other periods in my life when I was no worse by objective physical standards but felt so miserable that I dared God to strike me dead.

One of the factors that accounts for my change in attitude and feeling of well-being is what Dr. Oliver Sacks calls "accommodation."[1] Accommodation in this sense does not mean "surrender": It means accepting and making the best of one's situation. Accommodation is both psychological and physical. And it includes painstaking attention to the details of living, such as diet,

---

[1] Oliver Sacks, *Awakenings* (Garden City, NY: Doubleday & Co., 1974), p. 226. Note: If you are not familiar with parkinsonism and current treatment of it, you may want to read Appendix 1, "What is Parkinsonism?" before beginning Chapter 1 of the narrative.

exercise, rest, and recreation. Other factors are the effects of love and of doing things for others.

About three years ago my wife became terminally ill with breast cancer. I had thought that I couldn't manage without her help, but she became so ill that I felt the need to reverse roles and take care of her. The new relationship revived her feelings of love and respect for me. Her expressions of love had a strong therapeutic effect which continued even after her death.

I learned that helping others helps me as well. After my wife's death, I tried to give special aid and comfort to my four children. On a larger scale, I helped organize the Parkinsonian Society of Greater Washington.

Love continues to be a sustaining factor in my life—the love of family and friends; and for the second time in my life I have experienced a mutually loving relationship with a wonderful woman. As I look back at my life I see the power of love—as important as any drugs in helping me cope with parkinsonism.

Postscript from Donna Dorros

As many of you may know, Sid's book was the first autobiographical account of what it is like to live with Parkinson's. It was the beginning of what he considered to be his most important work, that of helping other Parkinsonians have more fulfilling lives. He had always wished to have his book available to people in the UK. He had many friends in England and had met many others there who had heard of his book and wanted copies. I am very pleased that Class Publishing thought Sid's book worthy enough to make it available to you.

Just a month after his final visit to the UK, Sid passed away very suddenly on 22 July 1993, from complications caused by his Parkinson's. Though he is no longer with us, I feel certain that he would be very happy to know that there is now a British edition of **Parkinson's: A Patient's View**.

Donna Dorros, 1998

Introduction to the British Edition

BY LES ESSEX

"I HAD BEEN diagnosed as having Parkinson's disease for six years before I read Sidney Dorros's book *Parkinson's: a patient's view*. When I was first told that I had Parkinson's I began to look for books and articles that would help me to understand what this meant and what the future was going to hold for me and my family. By far the most helpful book was this one by Sidney Dorros. Others were available, but only a few communicated so clearly the viewpoint of the patient. It was, and in my view still is, the best of its kind. At the time when I most needed this book it was almost impossible to obtain. Booksellers seemed unable to supply copies and the Parkinson's Disease Society of the UK was of the opinion (wrongly, I thought) that, as the book looked at an American with Parkinson's disease, it would not be helpful to patients in the UK, where the structure of the health and social services and medical care was so different.

After reading his book, I wrote to Sidney and commented that we had many things in common. We had both developed Parkinson's in our mid-thirties; we were both academics with young families to manage and needed to find strategies for coping effectively with the condition. Over the next few years we corresponded regularly and shared ways of doing battle to deflect the worst aspects of the disease.

In his book, Sidney describes the experience of being at

the forefront of new treatment, and being a guineapig for the National Institute of Health. They kept notes on his progress but so, too, did he. He kept detailed records and monitored his physical and psychological reactions, and the emotions that went with the changes. This gives a depth to his book and a fascinating insight into treatment, from brain surgery to new chemical drugs. Clearly in the last ten years there have been new developments in research, but this book provides the reader with an insight into how the most commonly used drugs work and interact with each other.

Throughout the book Sidney tells it like it is. He describes the difficulties that Parkinson's caused in his relationships, for example the lack of facial expression. When my own children complain that I do not smile at them, I think of Sid whose response to his own children was, "I'm sorry but I'm smiling inside."

I have often gone back to this book over the years and dipped into it when I have been faced with a particular problem. However, in rereading it in order to write this introduction, I am aware of how relevant it is to me still. For example, problems with sleep, which 15 years ago were not an issue for me, are now a major difficulty and I found some really valuable suggestions. The summary that contains the Ten Tips is particularly helpful. The message, "to make every day count" is both practical and inspirational.

What has stood out for me, and which is still of relevance today, is that, once diagnosed, the person with Parkinson's becomes the expert. This may not suit everyone, as some prefer to leave everything to the medical profession, but for those who wish to be active participants, taking major responsibility for the management of their disease, then this is the book.

Les Essex, 1998

About Les Essex:

Les Essex, a University lecturer in Social Work, was diagnosed with Parkinson's disease when he was 37 years of age. He then joined the Parkinson's Disease Society and served on the Society's Council of Management for 11 years, on the Welfare Advisory Panel and the Welfare Research Group. He helped produce a video entitled *Accommodation without surrender*, which is the subtitle of Sidney Dorros's book. This video was made by the University of Birmingham TV unit. Les has also been involved in the development of the National Institute of Conductive Education in the UK.

PHASE I

Early Symptoms and Treatment

1 Something Wrong

PARKINSONISM does not suddenly attack its victim. It sneaks up on one—slowly, quietly, but inexorably. Its initial signs are so subtle that Margaret Bourke-White, famous *Life* photographer, in writing about her heroic battle with parkinsonism, referred to the first evidence of the condition as a "wisp of a symptom."[1] In her case it was a slight dull ache in her left leg which she noticed when she climbed stairs.

In my case it was a slight ache in my left shoulder and then a hint of a tremor in my left arm while raking leaves on a beautiful Indian summer day in October 1960. I attributed the ache to fatigue; my wife thought I wanted to avoid an unappealing task—and we both thought little of it. But the ache in the shoulder did not leave with the leaves of autumn. So I consulted a physician, an internist. He diagnosed the condition as bursitis and suggested a shot of cortisone.

"It only hurts when I do something like rake leaves." I told him. "I'd rather quit raking leaves than risk the possible ill-effects of a drug as strong as cortisone."

"Hmpf!" he snorted, "I can't do anything else for you."

When I told my wife about it, she too said, "Hmpf!"

---

[1] Margaret Bourke-White, *Portrait of Myself* (New York: Simon & Schuster, 1963), p. 359.

But she did do something to help my shoulder. She raked leaves.

That was the first of many burdens that she took on as the symptoms of parkinsonism gradually stooped and stiffened me.

Debbie was already working harder than the average suburban housewife. For one thing, we had more than the average 2.4 children per family: we had four. In 1960, our children ranged in age from one year to ten. They were all active and called for a great deal of attention; but I was less available than the typical, middle-class, suburban father. I was a "workaholic."

Throughout my career I had consciously or subconsciously chosen to work much harder than was demanded of me—first, from 1947 to 1953, as an elementary school teacher, vice-principal, and principal, then from 1954 to 1957, as director of communications and research of the Maryland State Teacher Association (MSTA).

In January 1957, I assumed "a challenging opportunity" as director of the Publications Division of the National Education Association (NEA). When I arrived I found the editorial-production unit of "the world's largest publisher of educational materials for teachers" to be so short-staffed and demoralized that important information handbooks and department yearbooks were from several months to a year behind schedule.

In my eagerness to correct this situation and other problems, I abandoned a basic principle of good administration: Stick to managing. I not only reorganized and redirected the staff, but I plunged into production myself. I wrote, edited, proofread, and designed publications. I promoted and sold them at exhibit booths. I traveled all over the country and then labored late at the office to catch up when I got back. On a few occasions I stayed in the NEA building all night, catching a few hours of sleep on the custodian's greasy couch—even that short rest interrupted by mysterious noises from the boiler room. I brought home fat portfolios of work for evenings and weekends. And incredible as it seems to me now, in 1960, the year I quit raking leaves, I also began studying for a doctorate in education at The George Washington University.

Years later, when the incapacities caused by parkinsonism left me with much time for reflection, I suffered severe pangs of regret and guilt over the years I had neglected my family. Instead of being kept from my wife and children by the usual after-work "happy hour," I had been detained by attendance at afternoon and evening classes—dubbed by a tired classmate, the "unhappy hours."

But at that time, I ascribed my frenetic work pace to devotion to the cause of education, to which I was as committed as a missionary is to his religion. I would have been offended if someone had attributed my hyperactivity to ambition, or a lack of recreational interests, or inability to relax, or imbalanced body chemistry. Now, I believe that all of these, as well as idealism, were factors.

I have often wondered how much my workaholic ways may have contributed toward the unusually young age at which parkinsonism affected me and its rapid progress. Several physicians have told me that although hard work and other stress-inducing factors probably do not *cause* parkinsonism, they could *accelerate* and *accentuate* its symptoms. Perhaps it is no coincidence that the man who was the youngest administrator in his school system, the youngest member of the Montgomery County Education Association

Executive Committee, and the youngest division director at the NEA became the youngest Parkinson patient
in the L-Dopa trials at the National Institutes of
Health.

I wonder, also, whether my compulsion to work as
if time were running out may not only have been a
cause of the rapid onset of parkinsonism, but also an
effect of the condition; for parkinsonism includes ten-
dencies to hurry (festination) as well as to go slow.

I theorize that if the tensions of parkinsonism were
building inside of me, it is possible that aspects of
festination may also have been at work. This phenomenon is described by Dr. James C. Button:

> It may be that a patient's individual personality
> compels him to express a basic urge to "hurry." He
> tends fundamentally to be a dynamic, tense, driving
> type of individual. It is not known whether this type of
> personality actually predisposes its owner to the devel-
> opment of Parkinson's Disease, or whether the symp-
> toms themselves aggravate the personality type. It is
> probably safe to assume that such a personality, how-
> ever materially successful it may render its possessor,
> does tend to produce or at least to aggravate the
> symptoms of Parkinson's Disease.[2]

Now it may seem odd to feel the effects of the
disease before the first visible symptom. But the development of this mysterious malady is so slow that it is
possible, I believe, for it to affect people's feelings and
behavior long before any symptoms appear. Medical
authorities believe there may be a period of twenty to
twenty-five years between the damage to brain cells
that cause parkinsonism and the emergence of identifi-
able symptoms. It seems likely to me, therefore, that

---

[2]James C. Button, *Hope and Help in Parkinson's Disease*, 2nd ed. rev. (Norman,
OK: Button, 1964), p. 25.

parkinsonism affects a person inside long before it is recognized from the outside.

In fact, reflection upon my preadult years brings to mind conditions and incidents that suggest the beginning signs of parkinsonism as far back as my childhood. For example, during my late childhood my parents complained that I looked sad or angry in family photographs. Now, when I look at some of those pictures I think my expression foreshadows the frozen look of "parkinsonian mask." I recall, also, that after a physical checkup during my mid-teens, the physician wondered aloud why I was so "phlegmatic." And in my early twenties, when I was teaching sixth grade, one of my students said, "You should smile more often, Mr. Dorros. You look so great when you smile; but when you don't, you look so sad."

Regardless of the reasons for my workaholism, how appreciative I am now of those times given over to family fun. For despite my heavy work schedule, my wife and I and our two older children, Arthur and Ellen, did manage to squeeze in a number of family activities that we remember with great pleasure. Our special memories are the family camping trips we shared—en route to the NEA convention in Chicago in 1955 and "real vacations" at Swallow Falls and Deep Creek lake—in addition to the local hikes and expeditions that we went on whenever we could.

But David and Carol were born five or more years too late to acquire the same kind of reservoir of favorite things to remember. Neither remembers me before the symptoms of parkinsonism began to appear. David, especially, seems to have accumulated more memories to resent than to be glad about. Perhaps it has seemed so because he was the only one of our children to run away from home, which he did more than once. I remember the first time—he was about four years old—for another reason. It showed me how emotional stress can stimulate the appearance of parkinsonian symptoms.

When the children had started bumping into each other and us in our home in Bethesda, Maryland, we converted our garage into a combination den-study-and-playroom. It became everybody's favorite room, and it took some struggling to maintain its sanctity as a study when I used it to work on my doctorate. David, especially, seemed to resent being crowded out by a typewriter and his father.

He expressed this very dramatically one day in the spring of 1962. I was inside studying, and Debbie was driving the two older children to Sunday school. The roundtrip took about forty minutes, so she had instructed the two remaining children not to disturb me, not even to go in the house while she was gone. We later learned from Carol that as soon as my wife left, David fumed, "If I can't go in my own house, I'm running away! You want to come?"

"I wanted to go with him," Carol told us, "but I was afraid to cross the street. So I just stood on the corner and cried."

David did cross that street and many others as well. He was gone for so long we advanced from searching for him ourselves to recruiting the help of neighbors and, finally, to calling the police. It was the police who found him a few miles from home, still angry and still determined to get away. He was brought home against his will and promptly scurried under a table in the den. As I tugged at him, frustration, anger, and guilt churned within me, and a slight but definite tremor flicked through my left arm.

That was but one of several incidents that added to

my growing tension and vague feelings that something was going terribly wrong in my life.

2 Facing the Facts

TWO YEARS ELAPSED between the first "wisp of a symptom" in 1960—the ache in my left shoulder—and the first medical diagnosis indicating that I had Parkinson's disease. During those two years I experienced many problems which in retrospect are recognized as signs of the dread disease, but which I then attributed to fatigue or tension.

When my fingers began to lose their nimble touch-typing pace, I thought it was due to typist's cramp. When my wife pointed out that my shoulders seemed to be more rounded than usual, I thought I was too tired to sit or stand up straight, or perhaps I wasn't getting enough exercise, or maybe I just had bad posture habits. I would often get impatient, nervous, restless, or irritable, which surprised my family and friends. This too was attributed to fatigue.

It was our family physician and friend, Bob Jones[1], who first recognized that I had symptoms of parkinsonism. Bob was an ideal general practitioner—broadly knowledgeable, considerate, and available. He lived in the community he served, and he even made house calls. He dealt with the patient and his or her idiosyncracies, not just the ailment. He had a zest for life that was infectious.

---

[1] In order to protect the privacy of the doctor-patient relationship, all names of personal physicians mentioned in this book are fictitious.

During a routine physical checkup, I told Bob of the slight ache and tremor in my left shoulder and arm. He noticed that I didn't swing my arms freely when I walked, that my movements were a bit slow, and that my facial expression was somewhat frozen; but he didn't announce these observations at the time.

"You may have a neurological problem," he said. "I'd like a neurologist to check you out. I know a good man, Jim Walker. His office is across the county, but he comes to Suburban Hospital. I'll arrange to have him see you there."

It was typical of Bob to seek the easiest path for his patient. It was also typical of him to call and make the arrangements personally and immediately. The next day I had a consultation with Dr. Walker who seemed as friendly and considerate of his patients as Bob Jones was. Apparently it didn't take him long to recognize the symptoms of parkinsonism; but since he thought thirty-seven was an unusually young age for contracting the ailment, he had a few tests done to be sure the symptoms weren't due to a tumor or other cause. He had X-rays of my head taken and an electroencephalogram made.

The latter procedure is a simple, safe technique somewhat like the more familiar electrocardiogram. To get an electroencephalogram, electrodes are attached to the scalp and connected to a machine which makes a written record of the electrical signals emitted by the brain. Trained readers of the wavy lines get clues as to whether there may be a tumor, damage from a stroke, other abnormality, or a need for further investigation.

About a week after the initial examination, I got the diagnosis from Bob Jones. He took the time and exercised his skill to minimize the trauma when he broke the news that I had parkinsonian symptoms. He said that the ailment follows many different courses, and that some cases progress very slowly, or arrest themselves, or are limited in their symptoms. He told me that I didn't require any medication at the time but that there were medicines and exercises that could alleviate the symptoms considerably.

The remark that stuck, though, was one which could be comforting only if a doctor already had established good rapport with the patient. He said, "You'll probably die of something else before parkinsonism gets you. In the meantime, make the most of life while you can." Referring to an outboard engine that I had recently bought from him, he added, "You'll wear out that engine long before you have trouble running it."

I did wear out the engine, but not before I had trouble running it, for both the engine and I deteriorated more rapidly than Bob anticipated.

Superficially, I went along with my designation as a parkinsonian, but deep inside of me a voice said, "It can't be!" And for nearly a year, I really didn't accept the diagnosis.

"Bob Jones said it doesn't usually affect anyone younger than forty," I told my wife. "Maybe they're wrong. Maybe it won't get any worse."

Debbie, who had been trained as a nurse, knew more about the illness than she revealed at the time. Years later, I learned that she had seen parkinsonians in the last stages of the illness, during her nurse's training. Her recollections were so depressing that she set up a protective mental screen against believing that her husband could ultimately become as debilitated as the people she had seen. However, as my symptoms persisted, she helped me seek further medical opinions.

At the suggestion of my Uncle Louis, early in 1963, we consulted "the biggest" neurosurgeon in Washington, D.C. Dr. Taylor was so busy he had no time for amenities, barely enough time for examination of patients, and little time to talk with them about the examination. In the course of the examination, the neurosurgeon found that my facial expression had some mask-like rigidity, that I had some loss of movement on the left side, and that I held my left hand stiffly. He noticed no tremor at the time. His conclusion was that I might have an early Parkinson's syndrome; but he wasn't certain, and he didn't have the time to discuss it in any detail.

"What do you think the outlook is? How fast is—"

"I've got to leave for the hospital now," he answered. "Get another opinion. From a neurologist who specializes in Parkinson's." Before propelling Debbie and me to the door, he gave us the name of a Dr. J.B. Blade who practiced in Baltimore.

In contrast with Dr. Taylor, Dr. Blade was downright bountiful with his time. He took a detailed history, gave me a thorough examination, and discussed his findings with Debbie and me. In addition to the symptoms previously noted, he detected rigidity, typical of parkinsonism, at the left wrist and had me go through movements which revealed a slight tremor in the left hand. He said that I was too young to have what he called a "spontaneous" case of parkinsonism— that is, one not attributable to a specific cause such as encephalitis, carbon monoxide poisoning, or exposure to manganese. He thought that perhaps I had had encephalitis when I was very young and it was not recognized as such.

Reflecting upon my medical history from the perspective of present theories concerning causes of parkinsonism, I can see several possible causes of my condition. Most likely is an unknown virus or viruses.

I didn't know at the time Dr. Blade examined me in February 1963 that my mother and father were also parkinsonian. My mother knew but hadn't told me, and my father was not diagnosed until 1966. My only sibling, a brother who is four years younger than I am, shows no sign of the ailment even now, twenty years after my early symptoms. In recent years, therefore, doctors and I have tried unsuccessfully to identify a possible cause—an illness, an accident, or environmental condition—that affected my parents and me but not my brother.

Although he could identify no cause, Dr. Blade did convince Debbie and me that I had Parkinson symptoms, and that I should seek treatment. He thought that drugs such as Artane would give me considerable relief. I put myself under the care of Bob Jones for treatment and he prescribed a small amount of Artane and a tranquilizer, Equanil. The Artane made my mouth feel dry, and made me feel different in ways that frightened me although I couldn't describe them clearly. The tranquilizer, on the other hand, made me feel more comfortable and, even without the Artane, reduced most of my tremor and some of my stiffness. It made me slightly groggy; but this was more noticeable to other people than to me.

When I prevailed upon Dr. Jones to drop the Artane, he reluctantly did so, but cautioned me against too much use of, or dependence on, a tranquilizer.

At that time my right side was hardly affected, and I could usually function quite well even without the tranquilizer, so I used it only sporadically. I managed fairly well until the late spring. Then, the work at the office and at the university reached a seasonal peak, and as pressures grew, I experienced more tremor and stiffness on my left side and general feelings of uneasiness.

When I told Bob Jones about this he said, "Parkinsonism often develops in spurts, called *crises*. The symptoms go along on a plateau for a while, and then spontaneously or after a stressful condition, they become worse. I think you may be having one of these periods now. I suggest you go back to Artane."

"But Bob, the tranquilizer seems to give me such relief. I wonder if my problem isn't really just tension," I blurted out desperately, again hoping to escape from the diagnosis of advancing parkinsonism.

Bob flushed but quickly recovered his composure. "Before you diagnose yourself," he said, "I'd like you to see a good friend of mine who has just started private practice as a neurologist. He's had very broad experience in medicine. I studied under him at Georgetown University. His specialties were internal medicine and neurology. He was also chief of staff at the hospital where I had worked. He's one of the most brilliant and humane doctors I know. Several years ago he almost died of a heart attack and during his recuperation he did advanced studies in neurology. So he's right up to date on the latest developments. I think you'll like him, and if anyone can diagnose your condition accurately and help you cope with it, he can."

I hastily explained that I had reacted emotionally and that I was not doubting his competence as a physician. Nevertheless, I agreed to see Dr. Sharp.

As I returned home from Bob's office, I wondered why I still doubted the diagnosis of parkinsonism. I remembered that ever since early childhood, I had harbored a secret desire to accomplish something memorable in service to mankind. Suddenly I understood. I had been afraid that by accepting the diagnosis I would lose all hope of realizing this dream.

I've since come to believe that many other people, for reasons of their own, carry within them equally strong drives and aspirations. These strongly affect a person's reactions to a chronic ailment such as parkinsonism and need to be recognized, understood, and somehow accounted for by the patient and those who wish to help him. This is not easy when the motivations are well hidden.

In my case, after discharge from the army in 1948, I went to Teachers College, Columbia University to prepare to be an elementary school teacher, with the modest goal of eventually becoming principal of a school.

Even when I bared my plans and hopes for the future to Debbie, whom I courted at that time, I did not reveal—even to myself—my submerged dreams of great achievement. The closest I came was to cite the cliché about making the world a little better place than it was when I came in. I thought I could accomplish this through teaching, and I felt she would do the same through her career of nursing. Debbie and I also shared the desire to have five children and to raise them so well that they would be a joy not only to us but to the world. We felt confident that our combined training in education and health would make them five of the happiest, most fulfilled, and fulfilling people in the world.

However, by the time we'd had four children, we had begun to feel that teachers and nurses did not enjoy any magic advantage in rearing children. Perhaps our standards or aspirations exceeded realistic possibilities. For as the children grew older and began to

experience the problems of growing up and to assert
independent personalities, not always to our liking, we
began to wonder what we might be doing wrong. Was
I guilty of neglecting my family? Was my illness
affecting them?

These questions were on my mind the day in July
1963 that I went to see Dr. Sharp; and to my surprise
he seemed to read my mind. In taking my medical
history, he went beyond the usual simple questions:
age and sex of children, age of wife, family's general
health. He discreetly questioned my perceptions of my
family and my relations with them. In later visits it
became clear that he considered family relationships
an important aspect of patient health and therefore
added counseling on such matters to the many roles he
filled.

As Bob Jones had told me, James Sharp was a man
of broad interests and abilities. His examination of me
and explanation of my symptoms were even more
thorough and painstaking than those of Dr. Blade. I
was embarrassed when he revealed that he knew from
the reports Dr. Jones had sent him that I had resisted
accepting the diagnosis of parkinsonism. But he tried
to reassure me.

"It's understandable—to react as you have. The
mind resists unpleasant news. And it's easy to find
other explanations for early Parkinson symptoms.
Sometimes it's important to have the same questions
answered over and over again. But we can save a little
time by giving patients information in writing. There
isn't much medical literature available on Parkinson's
disease; but I highly recommend the autobiography of
Margaret Bourke-White, the *Life* photographer."

Shortly after my first visit with Dr. Sharp, I did read
Margaret Bourke-White's book. Coupled with the

doctor's counsel, the reading helped me accept the diagnosis of Parkinson's—permanently. Somehow I felt better after reading that she had experienced some of the same problems and fears that I did, and I was inspired by her apparently successful struggle to overcome them.

3 On the Brink

> . . . Start by selecting a personal physician who is accessible, whom you trust, and who has the time and patience to manage your general medical care, advise you about things you can do to help yourself, and counsel you concerning specialists whom you should consult. He should then give you his own opinion about the advice you receive from the specialist.[1]

This is the kind of physician Dr. I.S. Cooper recommends for patients with neurological ailments. This is the kind of man Bob Jones chose for me when he recommended James Sharp. He was the kind of doctor who could help a parkinsonian lead a fairly normal and productive life in the early stages of parkinsonism even without the powerful new drugs.

Bob had told me that Dr. Sharp had always been a sensitive, humane doctor. Apparently, his personal brush with death increased his empathy with and understanding of his patients' psychological as well as physical problems. And perhaps because his own health did not permit the hectic work schedule practiced by so many physicians, he gave me that precious gift—time. Our visits were seldom less than half an hour long, and he was rarely more than a few minutes late for an appointment.

Dr. Sharp explained thoroughly the nature and

---

[1] I.S. Cooper, *Living with Chronic Neurologic Disease* (New York: W.W. Norton & Co., 1976), p. 80.

19

treatment of my symptoms, how each medication worked, and what its limitations and side effects might be. He taught me to adjust the exact dosage of my medications to reach the delicate balance between undermedication and overmedication. He called this adjustment "staying on the brink" because, he said, "Most anti-Parkinson drugs don't have much effect until they reach the brink of toxicity. If you go over the brink, the harmful effects can outweigh the benefit of the medication. If you don't reach the brink, the medication will give you practically no relief from your symptoms. I can prescribe a basic dosage for you but there are many factors that can change the effect of the medication: your diet, type and amount of activity, amount of rest, emotions, even weather. So within the safe limits I give, I want you to adjust your medication to changing conditions."

He was talking about what are now old-fashioned medications such as Artane and Cogentin; but I found later that the same principle of staying on the brink seems to apply to new "wonder drugs" such as L-Dopa.

Dr. Sharp did not depend upon medications alone. Nor did he draw a sharp line of demarkation between his specialty of neurology and other medical fields or between my parkinsonism and the rest of my body functions. He occasionally referred me to specialists for consultation, but he didn't refer me to a battery of other doctors for treatment. He acted as neurologist, internist, and psychiatrist.

He prescribed an exercise program; made dietary suggestions; advised me regarding rest, sex, and family relations; suggested recreational activities; and counseled me on how to handle my work in more healthy, responsible, and satisfying ways. During each visit he allowed me adequate time to tell him of my symptoms, problems, fears, triumphs, and aspirations.

We even discussed religious faith and its important role in life and health. We both revealed that much as we longed for faith in a power outside of ourselves, we had difficulty believing the conventional concepts of God with which we had been reared. But I didn't tell that my faith in him had become almost spiritual in strength.

During the three years I was under the care of Dr. Sharp, from the summer of 1963 to the summer of 1966, I felt well enough and secure enough to live an active and full life. I planned for the future with little fear that I might eventually be incapacitated by parkinsonism.

Dr. Sharp encouraged me to continue all my activities and interests. Although the symptoms of parkinsonism slowly progressed, he kept me functional and fairly comfortable, first with the aid of Artane (2 mg, three times per day) and a tranquilizer, Equanil, a few times per day. In October 1964 he added one 2 mg tablet of Cogentin at bedtime. These medications enabled me to move fairly freely and eliminated the tremor on my left side most of the time.

When I asked him whether I should plan my life any differently because of my chronic illness, he responded with a story about Saint Francis of Assisi. Once Francis was asked, "Suppose, while hoeing your garden, you learned that the world was to end the next day; what would you do?"

"I would continue hoeing, *but a little faster*," he replied.

"And that's what I would advise you to do—even if *your* world were coming to an end," Dr. Sharp added. "But it isn't. There's a good chance your ailment can be controlled with present medical knowledge, and there's research going on which may well produce a cure." And so I vowed that I, too, would continue hoeing, but a little faster.

Dr. Sharp also told me I should walk about four miles each day. Normally I couldn't find the time for walking, but a lucky coincidence made it possible. In order to attend classes after work at The George Washington University, I had to drop out of my carpool between home and the NEA. With only one auto to share with my wife, I decided to ride the bus most of the time. Because I had to walk to and from the bus and between my office and the University, I came close to getting my needed four miles.

"You must get lots of exercise," Dr. Sharp said. "It won't just keep your muscles from deteriorating; it will reduce tension and tightness, help you rest better, improve your general body functions. For example, constipation seems petty, but it's a very troublesome problem for many parkinsonians. You can avoid it by exercising. Walking is the best all-round exercise. Swimming is very good, too." And he gave me some mimeographed descriptions and illustrations of sitting-up exercises designed by a physical therapist. I was told to do them regularly, especially in the morning and before going to bed.

Ever since I got that advice, I've been trying to walk the four miles and do the ten minutes or so of special exercises daily. I've found exercise to be essential to my well being, and I've learned, from talking with other patients, that those who have the most complaints are usually those getting the least exercise. Even knowing this, I occasionally have to relearn my lesson. I'll get busy, tired, or the weather will be bad and I'll use these as excuses to skip a walk or exercise session. I've invariably had to pay a heavy price for slothfulness in terms of stiffness, nervousness, constipation, and even depression.

How can you or someone you are concerned about avoid getting caught in the same trap? By forming regular habits of exercise. You must make it almost a reflex action: Do it at the same time every day; and like the mail carrier, you must not let rain or snow, sleet or storm interfere with your walk. If the weather is so bad that it is not safe to go out, I've found that pacing around the house, even if it does make me feel like a caged lion, is better than waiting for a "better time."

Swimming has posed a special problem for me, as I found it has for many other parkinsonians. While swimming, my breathing rhythm would occasionally falter and cause me to swallow water. The resulting sensation of choking set off a panic, especially if I was in water above my head.

Previously, I had been a good swimmer, accustomed to doing the crawl and sidestroke in which one exhales under water. After the onset of Parkinson symptoms, I tried for years to rebuild my endurance and confidence. But invariably I would falter in my breathing, swallow some water, and lose my confidence.

It was not until at least ten years after my swimming problems started that I accidentally found a way to swim with relaxation and pleasure. My wife and I began to use a YMCA pool which was heavily chlorinated. It burned my eyes so badly I instinctively tried to keep them out of the water. Imitating a friend who swam with her head up, I developed a sort of side stroke which kept my eyes and nose out of the water. This made breathing easier and I didn't swallow water when I lost my rhythm. Gradually, I was able to increase my endurance, and now I actually enjoy swimming instead of merely struggling at it.

"Exercises that you enjoy are much more beneficial than those done simply because they're good for you," Dr. Sharp told me. He also emphasized the value of engaging in activities involving other people. Therefore, he urged me to continue my favorite sports of golf and sailing. Even though Parkinson symptoms made it unlikely that I could shoot a low golf score, and even though the cramped positions involved in sailing were sometimes painful, he felt that these sports were good therapy. "If you get a kick out of sailing, that will loosen you up as much as exercise," Dr. Sharp said. "And since golf and sailing usually involve other people, the social contacts will be good for you, too."

And so, although I gradually became slower-moving, stiffer, and more tremulous on my left side, the years 1963-1966 were very busy and productive. They were also pressured and frustrating.

The year 1965 was especially crammed full. In February I was awarded the doctorate in education. The completion of that work was such a relief that for a few months I thought I was less stiff or tremulous, and I felt a flood of new energy which I expended both at work and with my family.

During the spring of 1965, Debbie and I took a memorable vacation in Nassau. That was the last time I was able to do any extensive bicycle riding without losing my balance. After our return, we moved to a new, larger house, this one even further from my office than our previous home. I was able to help with most of the packing, moving, and unpacking; I even did some painting in the new house.

In the summer of 1965, we took our last major family camping trip using a conventional tent. We had an old umbrella tent with a heavy wrought iron framework that had to be adjusted from the inside. It used to be a simple task for me to insert the center pole, raise the tent, and adjust the side posts while the children cheerfully hammered the tent pegs in. But now tent raising had become a major problem. Although our son Arthur, who was then fifteen, was capable of and willing to do the tent-raising, I was reluctant to give up my traditional job. However, when I crawled in the limp tent, I felt as if I were going to suffocate. I had difficulty moving the canvas to find the hole into which the pole was to be inserted, and when I tried to push the pole through, my tremors caused the hole or pole to move. I felt as if I were attempting to thread a needle in the dark. By the time I emerged from the tent, I was breathing hard and sweating profusely, and felt tense and irritable. This was the first of many periods of claustrophobia that I would experience as my Parkinson symptoms progressed.

Many other simple tasks became difficult. When some camping neighbors taught us to bake biscuit dough on a stick, I either burned mine or dropped it into the fire. On hikes, I tired more quickly than the rest of the family; so I either dragged along or waited for their return at the campsite. The park we were in, Douthat State Park, Virginia, had a beautiful lake, but I don't remember being in or on it very much. When swimming or boating time came, I often felt more inclined to take a nap.

Nevertheless, Debbie's patience and extra work, the children's enjoyment of camping, and my momentum in carrying on familiar and enjoyable activities obscured many of the problems caused by my Parkinson symptoms, symptoms that still were not usually evident to an observer. Our family color slide collection shows little indication of my Parkinson condition in the pictures taken during the summer of 1965. In fact, the most striking detail is how overweight I was then. I've since slowly lost thirty pounds—perhaps one of the few good side effects of having this ailment.

Around this time, pressures at work took on added dimensions as competition grew between the National Education Association and the American Federation of Teachers (AFT). Externally, the NEA was trying to cope with the threat of losing members to the rival AFT. Internally, it was torn by a fight between those who wanted to keep the NEA as a professional association, primarily devoted to the advancement of education, and those who sought, eventually successfully, to make it more like a labor union, devoted mainly to teacher welfare.

I believe that this intense organizational struggle and my reaction to it may have influenced the pace of advancement of my Parkinson symptoms. When doctors want to bring out symptoms of parkinsonism, they often create a condition of slight stress by asking a patient to do mental arithmetic while moving his fingers or moving his left arm up and down while the doctor manipulates the right arm. The slight competition of two different tasks often stimulates a tremor. What is the effect then of continuing stress caused by emotional pulls in different directions?

My frustration increased when I thought I saw a way to create a new type of organization that combined the objectives of labor unions and professional associations. But I found that my position in the NEA did not allow for much impact on policy. When I learned that my immediate supervisor was preparing to retire, I became eager to be promoted to his position where I could have more influence on the course of events. My eagerness was fed by some colleagues who encouraged me to think that I was a likely replacement.

Late in the summer of 1965, however, the appointment went to the director of another division, a person with much more experience and prestige in the organization. I liked and respected him and tried to accept the appointment gracefully. Nevertheless, strong feelings of frustration occasionally welled up inside of me and sometimes poured out. As the day the new boss was to take over approached, I began to have greater difficulty sleeping, my tremor was more frequent and severe, and I became a bit stiffer.

These symptoms caused Dr. Sharp to switch me from Artane to Phenoxene. After the switch I felt better for a while and hopped back on the fast train of activity at work and at home.

Early in 1966, however, I began to get symptoms that were noticeable to others. Slight tremor in my left hand was the first perceptible sign, but this could usually be temporarily alleviated or obscured by moving my hand and arm about or by resting my hand on some surface at the appropriate angle and level. My handwriting also became noticeably smaller and uneven. Sometimes I would have difficulty walking, especially after standing or sitting still for a while. At other times I would be unable to lift either foot. I felt frozen to the spot. But I soon developed a strategy for breaking the ice. I would kneel down and pretend to tie one of my shoelaces. This movement usually loosened my muscles enough to enable me to step out when I stood up. After a while, though, friends began to wonder out loud why I had to tie my shoelaces so often.

Like many parkinsonians, I was reluctant to tell people I had the ailment. However, when I thought that they were noticing and wondering about the symptoms I did try to tell them the cause as matter of factly as possible. I learned that people often misinterpret some of the symptoms if they don't know their origin. When I told them about my illness and its effects, it eased some of their concerns. For example, I remember one time while I was interviewing a candidate for a position in the Publications Division of NEA, I got the feeling she was becoming tense. I told her, "I have a chronic ailment of the nervous system called Parkinson's disease which affects my facial expression. So if I appear to be frowning at you or at your papers, please remember that I'm not really frowning. It's just tight muscles."

She immediately relaxed, "I'm glad you told me that. Thanks. I really thought I was making a bad impression or that you didn't like something in my record."

In her autobiography, Margaret Bourke-White wrote:

> If I could give only one message after sifting down this experience, it would be to urge others to banish the secrecy. I see now how futile are the obsessive efforts to keep the illness hidden. In most cases it isn't secret anyway, and it is the most harmful possible course to follow, because it robs you of the release of talking it over. I found that many of my friends knew all about it—in some cases they knew more than I. They were distressed most by not knowing how to help me. I was surrounded by a wall of loving silence which no one dared to break through.[2]

----

[2]Margaret Bourke-White, *Portrait of Myself* (New York: Simon & Schuster, 1963), p. 364.

I also wish that I had discussed my illness earlier and in more detail with some people. Somehow, I took for granted that they knew more than they did. In later years, I found that I had failed to talk about my parkinsonism with some of the people most important to me. My children, my parents and brother, certain close friends and associates at work have all told me that they didn't learn what was wrong until long after they had started worrying about me.

Children, especially, need to have the details of the illness explained to them lest they imagine a worse prognosis than is expected or build unrealistic hopes for a complete cure. One of our daughters, for example, used to ask me, "Daddy, when are you going to be perfect?" I probably should have explained that I would likely never be perfect, but instead I said, "Soon, I hope."

Another matter which should be discussed thoroughly with one's children is whether parkinsonism is inherited. I was unaware for several years that my children thought that it was a hereditary illness. At the time they first began to worry about it, there was some controversy about the question. It was clear that it was not directly hereditary in the sense that hemophilia or Huntington's disease is; but some doctors believed that a *predisposition or tendency* toward Parkinson's might be inherited in some families. Recent research, however, does not support heredity as a cause. Medical researcher Dr. Roger Duvoisin wrote in 1978 that "there is no evidence that the offspring of a patient with Parkinson's disease are at a greater risk of developing the disease later in life than anyone else."[3]

Dr. Duvoisin's statement has been reinforced since

[3]Roger C. Duvoisin, *Parkinson's Disease: A Guide for Patient and Family* (New York: Raven Press, 1978), p. 6.

by an ongoing study of identical twins which he is conducting in cooperation with other noted neurologists. This study is based on the assumption that if Parkinson's is hereditary identical twins would both tend to get the ailment. But the researchers announced in a second progress report in 1981 that the incidence of parkinsonism in both twins is no more than would occur by chance. Thus, they conclude that their study indicates parkinsonism is not inherited.

Shortly after I was finally convinced that I had been correctly diagnosed, I did tell my immediate superior and a few colleagues at the NEA that I had Parkinson's disease. But as the illness progressed, I was reluctant to describe the physical and emotional problems—sometimes caused by the ailment, at other times by the medications—that were not visibly evident.

Subtle changes continued; I realized that I tired more easily, that I was more tense and less patient and that I tended to avoid problem situations more than I had in the past. I also found it difficult to concentrate as intensely or for as long a period as I could before. The medication often made me feel sleepy or groggy. Since I was reluctant to admit, even to myself, that these problems were affecting my work, I tended to blame others for errors or inefficiencies which may have been due to poor planning or direction on my part.

The failure to communicate my condition was particularly damaging to the person I had previously worked with most closely, Donna Preudhomme. Donna, who started in the Publications Division as my secretary, was so efficient, hard-working, and enthusiastic that she soon rose to be office manager, and then production coordinator. For several years we kept each other fully informed about every aspect of our work. This took considerable time and energy but improved division efficiency. However, it became increasingly difficult for me to muster the necessary effort. I began to take shortcuts and tell Donna only the things that seemed absolutely essential for her to know. I also grew curt when she presented me with new ideas for improving production or publication sales, or called my attention to administrative or personnel problems that I was inclined to overlook. She interpreted this to mean that I had lost confidence in her, and it was one of the factors that caused her to resign from NEA employment in 1970. Except for a few notes—such as at the time of my retirement in 1973—we did not communicate again until 1977.

4 *First Crisis*

IN JULY 1966, I experienced a rapid and marked advance of Parkinson symptons. I had just returned from an NEA annual convention in Miami Beach, Florida. Overall I had functioned well at the convention, although I had to take periodic rests and had difficulty walking at times.

As soon as I arrived home, I called Dr. Sharp's office to reschedule an appointment that had been postponed because of the convention. There was no answer to my ring, not even a recorded message. I tried again later. Still no answer. I got a bit worried. Had Dr. Sharp's heart failed him?

Early the next morning I reached his secretary and asked how soon I could have an appointment.

"Not for at least six months," she replied. "Doctor is in Southeast Asia doing a special research project for the government. It came up on very short notice. He tried to call but you were out of town, and I know he was sorry to leave without talking with you. But he did suggest that you consult Dr. Cole while he's gone, or, if you prefer, Dr. Marjorie Spencer is willing to see you while Dr. Sharp is away."

I could scarcely speak to acknowledge the message. I felt as though I had been dealt a stunning blow. As I put the phone in its cradle, my left arm trembled more violently that it ever had before.

32

I felt abandoned—particularly because this situation had occurred before. Our family physician Bob Jones had left private practice to take a position with the Food and Drug Administration.

With Dr. Sharp suddenly gone, my attitude toward parkinsonism turned sharply downward, and my symptoms grew more severe. Before this period, the condition was only one problem in my life: a serious but not a dominating one. After he left, it became *the* problem, not only for me, but for my wife and children. When James Sharp departed for Southeast Asia, a good part of my confidence and ability to function seemed to go with him.

As I've already indicated, even before the doctor left, there were signs that my ailment was advancing. This turn for the worse might have been just as severe and rapid had he stayed. I'll never know for sure. But that experience causes me to suggest that if you are choosing a doctor to treat a chronic illness such as parkinsonism, you should consider whether his or her age, state of health, and future plans make it likely that he or she will be able to treat you for a long time. I'm not suggesting that you get a health report from a prospective doctor, and even though no doctor can guarantee long-term availability, I believe it is worth asking something like, "Do you foresee anything that would interfere with your continued availability to treat me for at least ten (or whatever number you think is reasonable) years?"

If you don't dare ask the doctor that, take a guess yourself and add the answer to the criteria for choosing a personal physician mentioned at the beginning of the previous chapter.

The first doctor we were referred to, Dr. Cole, did not meet several of those criteria, as far as Debbie and

I were concerned. Debbie later recalled our visit to this professor of neurology at a local medical school, in terms of cold and gray. "His office was gray, he looked gray, his voice and manner were gray—I felt his heart was gray, too. He just didn't seem to care at all."

My muscles tightened as he coldly confirmed the progress of my symptoms but offered little encouragement or interest in treating me. I was relieved when he told me that Dr. Spencer—who had previously seen me as a research subject—had offered to assume full responsibility for my care at no charge. I readily agreed to the arrangement.

Dr. Spencer was conducting research on the roles of genetics and of metabolism of minerals and metals in parkinsonism. She was particularly interested in my case because both my mother and father had the ailment. Previously, she had taken my history and collected urine and blood samples for study.

After I became her regular patient, she interviewed my parents and collected similar samples from them, also. Finding no significant indicators, she decided to try comparing the content of my cerebrospinal fluid with that of a normal control, that is, a person who did not have parkinsonism. My wife volunteered to be the control.

This was our first experience with a research procedure that had enough risk in it to require "informed consent." First, we learned from Dr. Spencer that the ethics of medical research require that any experimental procedure be done with the full knowledge and consent of the subject, and that if there is any danger involved, the potential benefit to the patient should outweigh the known hazards. The signed consent of the patient should be obtained prior to the procedure. If the patient is not competent to judge, the person legally authorized to make such decisions must sign. The paper one signs should contain a description of the procedure and list any drugs to be used.

In practice, I've found that the written description needs to be, and usually is, supplemented with an explanation to the patient in understandable language. The plan to be used in an experiment or research procedure is called a "protocol." Before beginning, it is submitted to qualified medical experts to be sure it meets safety as well as scientific standards. Thus, the experimental patient, in responsible and ethical hands, is carefully protected; and most researchers are no doubt ethical. There are, however, exceptions; and because one's life or health may be at stake, the patient and his family should carefully consider each procedure to be sure that their decision is an informed one. *Understanding* is the key word, because emotional pressures can warp the interpretation of the same words in the mind of either the patient or the researcher. Sometimes the patient, desperate for relief, interprets the potential benefits more hopefully than the investigator intended to convey; or the researcher, accustomed to certain "routine" procedures, underestimates the danger, or at least the discomfort, fear, or trauma for the patient.

Marjorie Spencer was certainly an ethical and responsible researcher. She explained in detail what I call the "Four Ps" of medical experimentation: purposes, procedures, possible dangers, and potential benefits. The purpose of her study was to see if there was a difference in the iron content of the cerebrospinal fluid of a parkinsonian as compared with a normal person. The procedure was to make a spinal tap, or medically speaking, a lumbar puncture, and withdraw a small amount of the fluid which flows around the spine and into the ventricles of the brain. Dr. Spencer explained that this very common procedure is usually quite safe, but with an area as delicate as the spine there is always some small danger of injury through accident or infection. The potential benefit to me would be very indirect and remote. If the results pointed toward a cause of parkinsonism, further research along this line might eventually be of help to me or others like me.

Dr. Spencer made it quite clear that I should not expect a cure to result from her findings. But although I said I understood, and, intellectually I did, emotionally, I built up overexpectations. I was like the purchaser of a lottery ticket who knows the odds are against him but still dreams of winning first prize.

As it turned out, the procedure had a serious effect on my wife. After our lumbar puncture, Dr. Spencer told us to take it easy for the rest of the day. But after a short rest in her office, she allowed us to return home. Debbie's interpretation of "taking it easy" included driving, sitting around the back yard, doing some minor gardening and her routine housework until she developed a headache accompanied by nausea and dizziness. She remained ill for several days and the incident frightened both of us. It also caused us to hope that the findings were significant enough to make Debbie's discomfort seem worthwhile. It was, therefore, very disappointing when Dr. Spencer told me that she didn't find anything in the spinal fluid to support the theory she was testing. This did not mean the effort was wasted, she explained. It added one more bit of information to the body of scientific knowledge that could be of ultimate use.

Again, I said I understood, but my stomach didn't. It knotted and churned in frustration, and my Parkinson symptoms became worse. Dr. Spencer changed my medication from Phenoxene back to Artane, but to no avail. Then she went out of town for a month or more. Again I felt abandoned and lost. According to notes I made shortly afterward, I "suffered greatly increased stiffness, tremors, mild nausea, aches in back and joints, and difficulty in sleeping because of vague feelings of tension, nausea and fear, especially when I stretched out flat. Even with my head elevated, these feelings often persisted to such an extent that I felt compelled to get out of bed and pace the floor. I also broke out in a cold sweat at those times and had spells of severe rigidity and tremor."

A mild sedative, Amytal, helped me sleep at night, but it caused me to be groggy much of the following day.

During Dr. Spencer's absence I turned to our new family physician, Donald Strong, for help. His attitude and manner were reassuring; and although he freely admitted he didn't know all he'd like to about parkinsonism, he thought he could handle my medical care in consultation with a neurologist. And so I went to see what must have been my fifth neurologist in Washington—this man highly recommended by a doctor friend who had worked with him. His report to Dr. Strong included the following description of my condition and recommendations for management:

> Neurological examination revealed the following positive findings: (1) Bradykinesia in gait, dressing and movements, (2) head and torso forward flexion, (3) bilateral flexion attitude of the arms, left over right, (4) propulsive gait with left leg drag, (5) tremor, rhythmical and somewhat regular on the left mixed with some smaller coarse irregular tremors of all the fingers, (6) rigidity, mild at right elbow, prominent in left arm, at elbow, and wrist, (7) left biceps reflex rapid, diminished right abdominal, (8) facial immobility,

only slight voice muffle, (9) mild Myerson, snout reflex present, jaw reflex brisk.

I believe that he has some bilateral but more prominent left-sided Paralysis Agitans.

Management should include: (1) current evaluation for surgery, (2) current physical medicine therapy for gait and daily living function, (3) return to Phenoxene in place of Artane, (4) Dexedrine or Ritalin may be helpful early in the day, (5) Equanil, Doriden, or Placidyl trial h.s.

This was the first time any physician had suggested the possibility of surgery. In fact, Dr. Sharp had said, "Whatever you do, don't even consider surgery unless I tell you it's advisable." But Dr. Sharp was out of the country, and Debbie and I had been reading reports of dramatically successful operations on parkinsonians.

A friend had shown us an old copy of *Life* magazine in which Margaret Bourke-White wrote of how Dr. Irving Cooper had relieved parkinsonism in her left side by deadening certain cells in the right side of the brain. (The functions of each side of the body are controlled by the opposite side of the brain.) In this classic article, vividly illustrated with photographs by her renowned colleague Alfred Eisenstaedt, Bourke-White credits Cooper with giving her life back to her. Following surgery she had to undergo extensive physical therapy but was then able to "practice the simple blessed business of living and working again."[1]

When we discussed the consultant's report with Dr. Strong he said, "I recommend surgery only as a last resort." His warning was based upon the dangers of permanent damage, or the rarer chance of death, that could result from surgery. But as he could offer no better treatment nor even any new medication still under development, we felt that we *were* at the point of

---

[1]Margaret Bourke-White, "Famous Lady's Indomitable Fight," *Life* 46:104 (22 June 1959).

last resort. The tremor and stiffness on my left side were getting so severe it seemed I would not be able to continue my work or much of any other kind of activity for long.

Debbie and I didn't know that a promising alternative to surgery had been reported in the medical literature. About half a year earlier, in an unpublicized article in the *New England Journal of Medicine* (February 1967), Dr. George Cotzias and his associates had reported their early results in treating experimental Parkinson patients with a Dopa compound. Either our physicians hadn't read the report or didn't think the results were conclusive enough to bring to our attention.

Years later I read the article which was entitled, "Aromatic Amino Acids and Modification of Parkinsonism." It described experimental use of a Dopa compound D, L-Dopa in which "8 of the 16 patients showed either complete, sustained disappearance or marked amelioration of their individual manifestations of parkinsonism." However, it also reported that many of the patients suffered a reduction of white blood cells after administration of D, L-Dopa. In a few cases the reduction was considered to be life-threatening.

"The sum of the evidence presented," wrote Cotzias and associates, "indicates DOPA is an effective agent for certain cases of Parkinsonism and worthy of further investigation. A similar long-term investigation with L-DOPA seems highly warranted as soon as it becomes economically feasible." We did not know, of course, that at the time we were convincing Dr. Strong to write a letter of referral to a surgeon in New York City, investigation with levodopa was already well underway.

The response to Dr. Strong's letter was prompt, giving us an appointment with Dr. King on July 12, 1967. In light of the cautions we had received about surgery, we planned to be evaluated by the surgeon, and, if he recommended surgery, to consult our physicians in Washington before deciding whether or not to have the operation. But our plans were changed by our exposure to a most remarkable combination of skill, medical teamwork, and salesmanship.

5 A Hole
in the Head

SOON AFTER DEBBIE and I passed through the old
stone hospital entrance that bore the inscription *Mt.
Olivet Hospital for Incurables*,[1] we began to learn why
Dr. Jerome King and the brain operation he performed
on parkinsonians were both so highly lauded and so
controversial.[2]

As we passed through the dirty, run-down lobby
and hallway of the old hospital on the way to the
neurological wing, I recalled comments I had heard
implying that Dr. King was a great self-promoter who
exaggerated the effectiveness of his operation and
played down the dangers.

"He'd need to do some promoting to get people to
stay in a place as depressing-looking as this," I thought
But the atmosphere changed as soon as we entered the
neurological wing. Suddenly the floor became soft
under our feet as we stepped into a thickly carpeted,
attractively decorated waiting room. Immediately we
were greeted by a staff of alert, friendly people.

Before we got to see Dr. King, we were processed by
an amazingly well-coordinated team. From the recep-
tionist, to the battery of doctors who examined me, to

---

[1]Not the real name of the hospital.
[2]The controversy still exists and is still relevant even though surgery is much less
frequently recommended, even by surgeons, since the advent of levodopa.
However, for those patients who do not respond well to levodopa or other
medications, a thalamotomy may offer the best possibility of help.

41

the charismatic Dr. King, to the administrative assistant who handled the business arrangements—each person seemed prepared for us, had read the reports that preceded us, showed some interest in us, and explained his or her role in relation to the rest of the staff. This evidence of managerial genius impressed me as much as Dr. King's deftness as a surgeon and his inventive skill in developing the cryoprobe—a surgical instrument used to freeze tiny portions of the brain.

I was examined by an internist, a psychologist, a neurologist, and a surgeon. Each checked to see whether I was a suitable candidate for surgery. Each interviewed my wife not only to get information about me but to ascertain and then shape her understanding of and attitudes toward the prospective operation. Finally, each doctor explained to us why I was a prime prospect for successful surgery.

By the time we reached the chief surgeon, we had become convinced that my relative youth, lack of ailments other than parkinsonism, and the nature of my symptoms made me a good candidate for surgery. We had been told that the risk of death was extremely slight and the risk of negative complications was only 1 to 2 percent, whereas the chance for alleviating the tremor on my left side was quite high (about 90 percent). The operation had been performed for over ten years, and many of the early patients still benefited from it.

It only remained for Dr. King to confirm the diagnosis. And he did. He seemed so relaxed, it was difficult to believe he had performed five extremely delicate and critical brain operations that morning. Within a few minutes, he convinced Debbie and me that he really cared about us.

After a brief discussion, Dr. King referred us to his

administrative assistant whom Debbie and I nick-
named Mr. Suave. Mr. Suave wanted us to decide
immediately whether to have the operation. We had
planned to think the matter over carefully—whether
to risk "a hole in my head" or wait for a possible new
treatment. But Mr. Suave said that Dr. King just
happened to have room in his schedule during the next
few days; that he usually was so busy with patients
from all over the world that if we missed this unusual
opportunity there was no telling when I might get
scheduled again; and by then I'd probably have to be
reexamined by the battery of doctors and might not be
declared a good candidate for surgery.

We were somewhat surprised at this hard sell, but
so strong was the confidence built up by Dr. King and
his staff that we made the crucial decision after a few
minutes in a private huddle, without consulting anyone. Mr. Suave quickly set a time and date for surgery
a few days away.

The next surprise came when he casually said, "To
save bookkeeping, most patients pay the surgeon's fee
in advance.

"They're not taking any chances with deadbeats," I
whispered to Debbie during another brief conference.

"No wonder everything's so posh in the neurological wing," Debbie added. But we did write a $2,000
check for the surgeon.

Four days later I was wheeled into Dr. King's specially equipped operating room. I was so confident and
relaxed that I entered the operating room more curious than fearful about the brain surgery that was
about to be performed.

I still remember the surgery as a most remarkable
performance—like an exquisitely orchestrated piece of
music or the home run that clinches a World Series.

I was kept fully conscious throughout the operation, for the reactions of the patient needed to be observed during the surgery. I had been told that neither the skull nor the brain itself feels pain; so that even without an anesthetic I would not feel the probe going in or the freezing of those cells whose destruction would free me from tremors and stiffness.

As I shifted from the mobile stretcher to the operating table, I caught a glimpse of the "jig," as I thought of it, set up at the head of the table to hold and guide the key instrument, the cryoprobe, into the brain. I knew that the cryoprobe, only about an eighth of an inch in diameter, was designed to carry a refrigerant whose temperature was 196 degrees below zero centigrade into its tip called the cannula. The setup reminded me of the machine shop equipment I had learned to operate at Brooklyn Technical High School. As I lay there, a thought flashed across my mind—if someone as clumsy as I could shape steel to tolerances of less than a thousandth of an inch with such tools, a skilled surgeon like Dr. King should be able to control his much finer equipment with incredible accuracy.

I did feel self-conscious and uncomfortable when my clean-shaven head was uncovered and firmly secured in a device that reminded me of a butcher's clamp for holding meat. The anesthesiologist, who was constantly at my side, explained that it was necessary for the head to be absolutely immobile in order to permit precision control of the instruments. I felt four prongs dig painfully into my skull until there was solid pressure and my head could not move. The only additional pain was from a few tiny jabs of a needle. The needle was used to inject a local anesthetic into a small area of the scalp that was to be cut back to expose the skull.

The deft incisions made by Dr. King were painless, but a few minutes later, the vibrations of a drill cutting a dime-size hole in my skull almost set off a wave of fear. The fear was stopped, however, by another recollection of my high school shop training: I remembered using a drill press with a check control on it. Even if my hand slipped, the check control wouldn't allow the drill to go any further than the distance set. I created a visual image of such a control on Dr. King's equipment. But I never did find out whether he had one. By the time the thought had flashed through my mind, Dr. King was saying,

"The worst is over. You won't feel anything now— just relief when we get the right spot. I want you to know that most of us will soon be leaving you for a few seconds. That will be to check our Polaroid pictures. We have to be certain that the probe is in exactly the right place. But we won't be long. It only takes about ten seconds for the pictures to be developed. And Dr. Borden, your anesthetist, will be here the whole time."

I expected to feel something, even if not pain, when the cryoprobe was inserted into my brain. But I don't recall any feeling at all. I did feel some pressure when air was substituted for some of the fluid in my brain. This was done in order to get clear photographs showing the location of the cryoprobe in the thalamus. It took two pictures to determine that the probe was in the right spot.

Now came the crucial and most ingenious part of the operation, a major advance in surgery devised by Dr. King. The area of the brain that seemed to be the right spot would be lightly frozen. My reactions would be observed, and, if there was a positive reaction and no indication of serious disability, the freezing process would be continued until a small number of cells were killed. But if the preliminary tests showed that the precise area had not been reached, this area would be unfrozen and the probe moved.

As the liquid nitrogen was pumped into the tip of the cryoprobe, I felt a relaxing wave flow through my body. The tightness of my fingers and the tension in my entire left side seemed to loosen.

"Count to ten," Dr. King instructed. "Now backwards." I had no trouble carrying out his instructions. This exercise, I knew, was to see that no damage was being done to my speech and thought centers.

"Now hold up your left hand and clench and unclench your fingers." To my great surprise, I could do so easily.

"Now move each finger up and down individually." Again I was able to follow his command.

"Wiggle your toes." They wiggled.

"Count to ten by twos. Now backward by twos."

"That's great. The operation's been very successful. We got the right spot the first time and won't have to go any further. We'll just finish the freezing process and you'll be on your way."

To finish, they fixed a plastic plate in position over the hole in my head. This and the other last details probably took longer than the crucial part of the operation, but I was in such a state of euphoria that time didn't matter.

I kept closing and opening the fingers of my left hand. I moved each finger up and down individually. And again and again I looked at that hand to make certain that the tremor had really stopped.

The sudden relief of muscle and nerve tensions created strange feelings in me. As I lay on the mobile stretcher in the recovery room, tears began to flow.

When I was wheeled out into the hall to where Debbie was waiting, I tried to stem my tears and smile, but when I felt her warm hand grasp mine and heard her say, "Dr. King says the operation was very successful," I burst into tears again.

Debbie recalled my first words, "Now I can get that job I want." This disturbed her greatly because she believed it indicated that my first priority was my work. I don't remember those words. Instead, I recall images and thoughts that flashed across my mind like a kaleidoscope. One of the pictures was of me in an influential position in the NEA. I also envisioned making love to my wife, driving down an open road with her next to me, walking through the woods with the children, playing golf, talking animatedly with friends, heeling over in a stiff breeze in a sailboat, and writing and typing with ease. I pictured myself demonstrating to all my loved ones the simple, exciting act of quickly opening and closing my left hand, moving my fingers, and holding my hand out with no tremor occurring.

These and many other visions flitted through my mind. I spoke of some of them later. Some were never verbalized. But getting a promotion at work was the first thing I spoke of, and this stuck in Debbie's memory and hurt her feelings and our relationship for a long time.

Of course, she didn't mention her disappointment at the time. She was soon busy aiding my recovery. And I needed her help.

When Mr. Suave urged us to arrange for the operation right away, one of his selling points was that room was available in the special wing reserved for Dr. King's patients where they received the best of care. I started out in a quiet, comfortable double room in that wing, but after the operation I was taken to a large room with five or six beds.

The dominant figure in the room was a large, regal-looking man. The white bandage covering his entire skull and a broad smile identified him as one who had recently had successful cryosurgery. This happy man, who had come from Greece for the operation, was constantly attended by a retinue of admiring and talkative relatives. It would have been difficult to rest with that much noise, had the sounds not been so pleasant. But the sounds made by two other people in the room not only disturbed me greatly at the time; they left me with fears that still haunt me. The two people were the wives of unfortunate patients who hardly moved or spoke. But the wives kept up bitter harangues, sometimes addressing their spouses, some-times a particular passerby, but usually talking or shouting to the world in general.

One was a middle-aged woman who maintained that her husband pretended to have Parkinson's because he hated her and was trying to spite her. She said he was a lazy, worthless worm. When he got home from work, he would just want to sleep. When she served him the supper she had worked hard to prepare, he slumped over and pretended he couldn't eat just to spite her. He said he couldn't walk at night, so he wouldn't have to take her out. He got out of cutting the grass and other work around the house by claiming to be stiff, she said.

"How come he could go to work but not do anything around the house?" she asked rhetorically.

"Because he probably used every ounce of energy to push through his work day," I wanted to answer for him. Then shouting in frustration directly at her silent husband she said, "I'll get even with you. One of these days you'll look up and I'll be gone. I'll just leave you!"

Almost matching the middle-aged woman in bitter commentary was a woman in her thirties, the wife of a rabbi. She, too, refused to believe her husband's illness was genuine; but she took a different escape route. She blamed her mother-in-law for causing all of her misery, including her husband's symptoms. I don't recall exactly how her mother-in-law supposedly caused the illness, but I remember the hatred and frustration in the woman's voice. And she, too, threatened to leave her husband.

I wondered if these two women had become mentally disturbed as a result of their husbands' illnesses or if their shrewishness actually aggravated the illness. I thanked my lucky stars for the supportive, sympathetic, and apparently patient manner in which my wife had accepted my ailment. But exposure to these women filled me with fear that Debbie, too, might ultimately be overwhelmed emotionally if she had to cope with much more of it. I wanted desperately to get us away from those unfortunate women. This was our first, but not last, experience with family members who apparently had cracked up under the strain of living with a parkinsonian. Debbie realized that exposure to that kind of noise would allow me little rest. Also the operation left more severe aftereffects than we had expected. I felt weak, groggy, and emotionally volatile. I could hardly speak. But we didn't need to discuss it. Debbie went to the administrative office and insisted on a change of room.

"But we have no other room," she was told.

"I'll stay here until you find one," she replied. They found one. It was a quiet room but, unfortunately, located in the regular part of the hospital, not in Dr.

King's special recuperative section. There was quite a difference.

This section was dirty, poorly staffed, and noisy all night with the jesting, laughing, and romancing of the staff. And the food so lacked in nourishment and flavor that I began to think I would suffer malnutrition if I stayed there too long.

Another thing that bothered me greatly during my stay in Mt. Olivet was the seemingly callous attitude of the paraprofessional and support staff toward the patients. Patients who cried out for help were forced to wait interminable periods, and when they finally got attention, it was often accompanied by verbal abuse.

Fortunately, the first few days I had special nurses around the clock. They were selected and instructed by Dr. King's staff to help the patient through the most critical postoperative period. This is the period when infection or other complications can cause death or serious brain damage.

I passed through this danger period without any physical complications. But sometimes the nights were fearsome. Although I had entered and gone through the surgery without much fear, now that it was over, it scared me. I dreamed about the crunching noise of the drill boring through my skull. I had nightmares in which I was paralyzed. But the worst nightmares were ones in which I heard Debbie screaming at me like the wives of those other patients.

My fears were soon allayed, however, by my wife's cheerful attention to my every want or need as she spent most of each day with me. Debbie brought me wholesome food to supplement the overcooked, undernourishing hospital meals and she watched over me each day. The importance of her attention in hastening my recovery and maintaining my morale

hung in counterpoint to the situation of my roommate, Bob Michaels. During the week or so we shared
a room, Bob had one brief visit from his wife and one
from his daughter. Even though the operation achieved
significant physical improvement in his condition, he
was as depressed when he left the hospital as when he
came in. Before the operation, he had trouble getting
food into his mouth or handling money in his job as a
bank clerk. He left the hospital with greatly improved
ability to function, but just as depressed as when he
entered. Before Bob left the hospital, however, he was
a participant in a verbal exchange that added to
tensions growing between Debbie and me.

After a week or so of long days at the hospital, my
wife's nerves were worn quite raw. She needed and
deserved a great deal of support and appreciation for
her intense attention to me. However, mixed with my
appreciation were the nightmarish images of the
shrewish wives I had seen. I feared that too much
contact with me in an ill state might make a shrew of
Debbie, too. I felt overprotected, overmothered. Also,
I was very tired, yearned for sleep and felt that Debbie
needed more rest as well. Subtle hints or requests that
she not spend so much time at my bedside didn't seem
to have much effect. So one day, when I was feeling
particularly tired and irritable, I blurted out the rather
unfriendly exclamation, "I wish you'd leave now!"
This affronted her greatly. And when my roommate
Bob chimed in with the comment "You should be
ashamed of yourself, speaking to your wife like that
after all she's done for you," Debbie felt doubly
justified.

For years afterward when she felt unappreciated,
and she often did, Debbie quoted Bob's words. In
retrospect it is very clear to me that I could have and

should have handled the situation more graciously and I should have shown more appreciation for the devoted care my wife gave me. However, the incident also has a message for those who, like Debbie, care for an incapacitated spouse: Give your loved one lots of attention, but try to leave some time for yourself each day to get a break from your ill partner and to get some enjoyment out of life. You needn't feel guilty about doing things for your pleasure when your spouse is lying sick in bed. Because when you share your experiences, you will share the pleasure, and this will make you a more exciting person to be with. It will also prevent the patient from feeling guilty for needing so much of your time because of his illness. It's not easy to strike the right balance between fun and none, but it's probably safer to risk erring on the side of too much fun rather than too little.

Although the routine nursing care in the unit I was in did not match the quality of care in Dr. King's wing, the well-organized team of the neurology department found my remote room and a flow of doctors and therapists came to test the results of the operation and to speed as full restoration of function as possible. The medical teams that made frequent check-up visits included surgeons, neurologists, internists, and psychiatrists. When I was too weak to move, a masseur came daily to stimulate my circulation and muscle tone. A physical therapist gave me a daily workout and provided me with a set of exercises to do at home. A speech therapist first came to my room, and then, as soon as I was able to get there in a wheelchair, I joined group therapy sessions. In those sessions I was surprised to observe how many patients did have at least temporary damage to their speech as a result of the surgery.

I noticed other kinds of difficulties as well. There was the dentist who was troubled only by a relatively mild tremor before the operation. He couldn't continue his practice, however, unless he could eliminate the tremor. The operation did that, but in exchange he acquired seriously slurred speech and difficulty in walking. He had been told that in about two weeks he'd be nearly fully recovered. But when I left the hospital, more than two weeks after his surgery, his speech and mobility were not much improved.

Several of the patients complained of new problems, ranging from poor memory to paralysis of a limb. I noticed that after surgery my left foot tended to turn in, and a previously existing limp increased. But exercise soon seemed to ameliorate these problems and I returned to Bethesda confident that when the hair grew back on my shaven head, I would feel, function, and look nearly normal.

But by the time the hair grew long enough to comb, I felt increased tremor and stiffness on my right side. I have since learned that a thalamotomy on one side often does hasten the progress of the symptoms on the other side. I don't think Dr. King's staff told me that, although they had suggested that I plan to come back to "do the right side" within a year. I had wondered why, because I previously had little trouble with my right side. But after seeing first-hand the damage the operation could do, I was very hesitant to risk a second operation.

People often ask me if I would have chosen to have the operation by Dr. King, knowing what I do now. The answer is, "Of course not!" But neither I nor anyone else knew at the time how soon a new drug treatment would be available that for me would be more effective and safer than surgery. One can only act

on the best information available at the time of decision. On that basis, I believe my wife and I made the
right decision.

Perhaps I wouldn't feel so smug if I had to wear a
brace on my leg, or had to relearn speaking, as did
some of my parkinsonian friends who had less successful operations than I. My major problem, in addition
to the already mentioned limp, is a difference between
my left and right sides in reaction to anti-Parkinson
drugs. Sometimes I feel as if I have two separate bodies
joined together like those of a Siamese twin. However,
I have been fortunate enough to have enjoyed almost
complete elimination of tremor on my left side for all
of the twelve years since the surgery. I have also
enjoyed considerable and sustained reduction of stiffness on my left side. Thus, I have been helped over
some rough spots by the ability to move my left side
before my right "uncorrected" side responds to medication. For example, for several years I was able to
shave with my left hand shortly after arising. By the
time I shaved and got dressed, also mostly with my left
hand and arm, my right side began to function with the
aid of levodopa.

So, on balance, I believe the hole in my head has
been worthwhile.

PHASE II
Experiences
with Medical
Research

6 Becoming an Experimental Patient

FOR A FEW MONTHS after my return from New York, I enjoyed the illusion that I had been cured. My children were exultant to see that the tremor had stopped, but they became impatient with my long recovery period and were embarrassed and worried about the hole in my skull, the shortness of my hair, and the large head bandage I usually wore. I returned to work still wearing a bandage, not realizing at the time how much I looked like an invalid.

The warm welcome I received at work buoyed my confidence so much that I again envisioned myself as a candidate for promotion. Again I dreamed of how I would apply all my experience and abilities to strengthen Information Services for the "new NEA." But again the position went to someone else and I experienced great frustration, which I tried to suppress.

The frustration and disappointment seemed to accelerate the advance of my Parkinson symptoms. Within a year after surgery, tremor and stiffness on my right side made the previous difficulties on my left side seem relatively insignificant. I tried professionally administered physical therapy, swimming and other exercise, and massages. These activities relaxed me somewhat and generally increased my feeling of well-being, but they failed to stem the progress of parkin-

57

sonism. In fact, if I passed even slightly over the thin
line bordering on overexertion, tremor, stiffness, and
difficulty in moving increased greatly. Not only were
the symptoms more acute, but since I'm right-handed,
tremor and stiffness on my right side became much
more disabling than they were on my left.

Much of my work involved typing or writing and
more and more frequently my fingers scrambled the
letters my brain was trying to get them to type; my
handwriting became smaller and smaller and wavier
and wavier. Then the speed of my writing and typing
slowed from a gallop to a slow walk, to a crawl, and
then froze at times to a complete stop. Some days I had
to wait hours before I was able to sign my name to the
daily stack of outgoing mail. I endured this frustration
for several months before I agreed to my secretary's
suggestion that she sign my mail for me.

By the spring of 1968, it seemed that only a major
new discovery in the medical treatment of parkinsonism could possibly save me from imminent incapacitation. A close friend who was a physician continually
reassured me that such a discovery would come soon.
He was a regular reader of the New England Journal of
Medicine and he vaguely remembered that a scientist
with a Greek-sounding name had reported in 1966 on
a promising new type of drug.

Then on a beautiful day in May 1968, my physician
friend triumphantly brought me proof that he had not
raised false hopes. "Parkinson Victims Reported Relieved by Drug in Tests," proclaimed the matter-of-
fact headline on page 49 of the May 8 issue of the New
York Times. The article reported that Dr. George
Cotzias had announced at a meeting of the Association
of American Physicians that his research group at the
Atomic Energy Commission's Brookhaven Labora-

tories had brought about some improvement in each of twenty-six Parkinson patients treated with L-Dopa. Some of the patients experienced very dramatic improvement. The article told of a film showing patients who once could neither walk nor feed themselves become self-sufficient and ambulatory.

"How can I get into Brookhaven to try L-Dopa?" I blurted out. "Should I write or call Dr. Cotzias?"

"Neither," my friend replied. "Most experimental programs will accept patients only on recommendation of a physician. Let's see what the medical journals have to report before you get too excited."

I waited, but I couldn't help getting excited. When Debbie and I discussed the possibilities, I pointed out that some patients at Brookhaven had been there for as long as two years. "Don't worry about how long it takes," my wife assured me. "If they can help you, I'll do whatever's necessary to get you there and to manage while you're gone."

At last, on May 27, 1968, the *Journal of the American Medical Association* reported "Modest to Dramatic Results" from "Dopa Used for Parkinson's Disease." Armed with a copy of the article, we went to see our family physician who readily agreed to write Dr. Cotzias requesting him to consider me for treatment. Five weeks later, the general practitioner called to read me Dr. Cotzias's response. Cotzias, who had been overwhelmed with similar requests, wrote on July 24, 1968:

"Unfortunately our group is extremely small and we are not in a position to see any new cases. I understand that centers in your general vicinity are taking up work similar to our own. It might be worth your while to refer your patient to one of these centers . . . ."

"Can you find out what those centers are?" I asked.

"I'll try," promised my physician. "I'll call the Neurological Institute of NIH. They should know. They may even be acting as one of the centers."

A few days later he phoned me with disappointing news. He had spoken to the doctor in charge of research on Parkinson's disease at the National Institutes of Health who told him they were not using L-Dopa at the Institute nor did he know of any center that had started using it other than Dr. Cotzias's.

"Be patient," my doctor urged. "I'll keep an eye out for news of an experimental center. I'll let you know as soon as I learn anything."

While I was waiting, a flood of articles appeared not only in the professional journals but in newspapers and popular magazines, all reporting astounding results from what some began to call the "miracle drug."

My hopes were raised again by news that a center would be opening in about a month to administer L-Dopa at a hospital in the Washington area, but months went by and the starting date was postponed several times.

Meanwhile, my wife and I and relatives and friends had our own intelligence network going. Scraps of information came in from relatives and friends in Worcester, Boston, New York, New Jersey, and the Washington area. I applied a communication technique a college roommate had taught me which he called "tel-a-person," also known as word-of-mouth. Anyone I came in contact with who might possibly know anything about the subject was told about my desire to try L-Dopa. And eventually, through an interesting stroke of fate, "tel-a-person" reached the right person.

That person was Bob Jones, my former family physician who had left private practice a few years earlier to take a position in the Federal Food and Drug Administration. Even though he continued to live in the neighborhood, I had lost contact with him until one fall evening I was pleasantly surprised to meet him at a Boy Scout meeting to which we had come with our sons. I lost little time in telling him about my search for L-Dopa.

"I may be able to help you," he said. "One of the things I do at FDA is to help process applications for the experimental use of drugs. And just today I remember seeing an application from a doctor at one of the National Institutes of Health to try L-Dopa with Parkinson patients. Tomorrow is my last day with FDA. Monday I transfer to the Justice Department. If you're interested, call me tomorrow and I'll give you the doctor's name."

"If I'm interested? You must be kidding!"

The next morning I called about one minute after he had gotten to his desk. It took only another minute for him to find the appropriate papers. He gave me his name and told me, "He's chief of the Unit on Neurology of the National Institute of Mental Health which is one of eleven institutes in NIH. That explains why your family doctor drew a blank. He phoned a unit called the National Institute for Neurological Diseases and Stroke, which was logical because it's the institute that's especially concerned with parkinsonism. But nobody in that institute has put in for permission to use L-Dopa."

"Isn't that strange," I thought out loud.

"Not at all," responded my friend. "Most of the research NIH sponsors is done by people at other research centers all over the world who get financial help from NIH but are not NIH employees. Only a relatively small amount of research is done at the facilities you see in Bethesda. The Institute for Neurological Diseases probably helped finance research in various institutions outside NIH that led to the discovery by Cotzias and associates at Brookhaven."

"Then why do you suppose the Institute for Mental Health is planning to experiment directly with L-Dopa on Parkinson patients?"

"That, you'll have to ask the NIMH neurologist. I can only guess that they want to study the mechanism by which L-Dopa works in the hope that it may have application to mental health. And since parkinsonism is the only illness for which L-Dopa is recognized as a palliative, they've got to treat Parkinson patients in order to get subjects through whom they can learn more about its exact effects in humans."

"In other words, if I entered that program I'd become a human guinea pig."

"In a way, yes. But as a human, there are laws and ethical practices to protect you. They provide that no drug or treatments should be tried on you unless the likelihood of its helping you outweighs any known dangers. Also, you have the right to informed consent. That is, you may agree or refuse to participate in any experiment after being told its objectives, procedures, and dangers. But why am I telling you all this? Call the neurologist at NIMH."

I did. And to my surprise I had no trouble getting through to him. Although he immediately reminded me that referrals are considered only if made by one's physician, he did tell me enough about his proposed program for me to decide that I wanted in; and he listened to enough of my history to determine that I was possibly a good candidate for admission. I was relatively young, in good health except for parkinsonism, both my parents had the illness, and I lived only a mile from the Institute.

After NIH received a referral letter and a copy of my medical history from my family physician, my wife and I were invited for an interview.

On January 15, 1969, Debbie and I entered a tiny examination room in the enormous Clinical Center of NIH. We were under great tension, which the size of the building and the complexity of the equipment we'd noticed on our way to the designated room did nothing to relieve. Initially, I feared getting lost in an impersonal medical bureaucracy. This concern was alleviated by the words and manner of the neurologist who interviewed us. He did not fit the stereotype of an introspective, impersonal researcher. As he asked questions about my medical and personal history and examined me physically, I got the impression that he was a very humane and competent physician, and that he considered me as a person, not just as an experimental subject. Still, after declaring me a good candidate for his research program, he explained very candidly that his primary purpose and that of NIMH was to add to scientific knowledge, not to treat patients.

"In deciding whether a person will be accepted as an experimental patient, the major criterion is how suitable that person is as a subject, not how badly he needs the treatment," he told us. "But, once the Institute takes on a patient, it gives that person the best possible medical care and the life and welfare of the patient are placed above the demands of research."

"Just what is the objective of your research?" I asked. His answer indicated that my friend at FDA had surmised correctly.

"To learn as much as we can about exactly how L-

Dopa works," he told us. "My special field of interest is neurological pharmacology—that is, drugs that affect the nervous system. Several years ago, before I came to NIMH and before L-Dopa was used with Parkinson patients, some of our investigators tried using L-Dopa to alleviate certain aspects of mental illness, particularly depression. The severe side effects, however, caused them to drop the study. Now that it's been demonstrated with Parkinson patients that slow build-up of oral doses to therapeutic levels can reduce the unpleasant or dangerous effects, we hope we'll find that L-Dopa can relieve other ailments. Then, too, if we learn more about how it works and affects the human body, the knowledge may help us find other, even more effective and safer drugs to treat a whole host of neurological disorders. One never knows what application basic research may have. It was basic research done at this Institute on the action of chemical neurotransmittors, beginning about fifteen years ago, that helped make it possible for other investigators to conceive of using L-Dopa to alleviate parkinsonism."

"We're both interested in aiding medical research," my wife stated, "but I'm most concerned with my husband's health. I'd like to be sure he'll get the best possible care."

"I think he would," replied the doctor-researcher. "I'm a qualified neurologist with experience in treating Parkinson patients. We'll have a staff of outstanding young neurologists assisting. Our nursing staff is very highly trained. Nowhere do you find a higher ratio of medical staff to patients, and we have the resources of the entire Clinical Center to draw on should your husband need any other specialized attention. We'll be responsible for his entire medical care, even if he catches cold. That's partly a service to the patient, but it's partly so that we'll have complete knowledge of everything that affects the actions of the drugs we're experimenting with."

A brief tour of the hospital wing where I would be housed helped confirm his statement about the quality of patient care at NIH. We were impressed with the friendliness and apparent dedication of all the staff members we met, including doctors, nurses, and aides. Following our tour, the physician reviewed the dangers accompanying trial of any new drug as well as the advantages of entering the program.

"You'll have to be hospitalized for at least six weeks to begin treatment with L-Dopa, then you can come in periodically for checkups and tests as an outpatient," he explained. "While you're here, however, you won't be confined to bed. All patients who're able to get dressed each day will find many things to do. In fact, if you wish, you can do some of your work here. We can even see that you have a typewriter."

"He must be optimistic about the effects of L-Dopa," I thought as I remembered how slow and laborious my typing was at the time.

He then told me I had a few weeks to decide whether to participate. I wanted to say, "I'm ready right now." But he seemed to read my thoughts. "We won't be starting for at least a month, anyway," he said, "so don't try to make up your mind right now."

But it didn't take us long. After consultation with our family doctor, friends and relatives, and my associates at work, we decided to accept what was obviously the best of all available opportunities.

7 Scared Stiff

AFTER I WAS ADMITTED to Nursing Unit 2-West on February 19, 1969, one of the first orders of business was a thorough physical by the young physician who had been assigned responsibility for my overall medical care. For over an hour and a half he probed, observed, questioned, listened, and recorded. Then he summarized: "You're in exceptionally good health except for parkinsonism, and that seems to be of only moderate severity. I see from your records, though, that you usually have more stiffness and tremor than you have now."

"Well, I've become more relaxed than usual since I was admitted to NIH. I find that when I'm relaxed my symptoms are considerably alleviated." I thought I was letting him in on a great discovery.

"I know," he said. "That's a common phenomenon in Parkinson's."

As he began to discuss my condition, I realized that he was advanced far beyond the intern level I thought he was at. Although he had only recently come to NIH, for a three-year stint, he had completed a residency in neurology at another hospital.

I later learned that one of the main functions of the NIH Clinical Center has been to train thousands of such carefully selected, unusually intelligent, and dedicated researchers. Relatively few stay on for careers at

NIH. Most go out to hospitals and laboratories all over the world to advance medical research.

The clinical associate went on to explain why a comprehensive physical and record of such were important both as a baseline for research and to protect my health: New drugs could affect one's organs or state of health in unexpected ways. Through blood and urine tests, X-rays and observations as well as other means, I would be constantly monitored to detect any changes from my condition upon entry.

Finally, he said the words I wanted most to hear: "You're a good candidate for the L-Dopa trials."

The nursing staff then oriented me and helped me settle for a long stay. Since my Parkinson condition seemed to be of "moderate severity," another early order of business was for the head nurse to help me borrow a typewriter from Occupational Therapy. Colleagues from my office then brought out a briefcase full of papers for me to work on. Until L-Dopa began to work its magic, however, I spent several weeks merely shuffling the papers.

Besides occupational therapy there were a number of other interesting kinds of recreational activities for patients. There was formal "physical therapy" plus informal sports and games in a gym and recreation room. There were crafts, movies, musical programs, and a well-stocked library. We even had our own Ping-Pong and pool tables in our wing. Participation in such activities often helped make visits actually enjoyable for my children. Carol, our youngest child, especially remembers the Saturday-night family movies and the family Carnival at which she won a prize. And David became almost a pool shark in the course of his visits.

My room was pleasant, attractive, and well-equipped—and so were most of the nurses.

Since I was one of the first patients admitted for the Dopa study and the unit didn't fill to capacity during my first stay, I enjoyed more space and staff attention than is normal even at NIH. This may have "spoiled" me enough to lead to difficulties later on.

But for the first few days my family, friends and I enjoyed the impression that I would be rejuvenated in an atmosphere as comfortable and enjoyable as a health spa.

Nevertheless, a week after that glorious admission day I wished I had never heard of NIH. I wished I were dead and I almost looked and felt as if I was a corpse.

Before I entered the hospital, the senior investigator warned that I would have to be taken off all medications for at least two weeks prior to starting on L-Dopa. There were two reasons for this: One was to analyze my condition and body functions in what doctors called "baseline state" (that is, my state without the help of medication); the other was to clear my body of other medication so that there would be no interference with the action of L-Dopa or confusion of its effects.[1]

"We don't know how stiff or tremulous you may become when we stop giving you Cogentin," said the doctor in charge. "So we're prepared to give you every help you may need should the lack of medication incapacitate you in any way. If you have any trouble dressing, washing, eating, or any other difficulties, keep calm, let us know, and we'll get you help. Remember, your problem will be temporary and we'll take care of you, so don't be frightened or discouraged

---

[1]Prior to entry, I had been taking Valium as a tranquilizer, Pertofrane as an antidepressant, and Cogentin to relieve stiffness. I had been instructed to stop taking Pertofrane and Valium before entering the Clinical Center and was taken off Cogentin two days after admission.

if you get stiff." He sounded very convincing and most of the staff did exactly as he predicted. But I didn't respond as well.

A few days after I went off all medication I became so stiff I had difficulty walking, eating, even turning in bed. After a few more days, I could move about only in a wheel chair and I had to be dressed, bathed, and fed by an attendant. I was not just frightened and discouraged, I was scared out of my wits.

I was scared for several reasons. The first reason was not a rational one. It might be described as a "gut" reaction. Many parkinsonians in advanced states of disability experience it and I believe have similar reactions. Perhaps it is a special kind of depression. Whatever it is, it is so frightening that when I am very disabled I feel close to death. Even when I've known for certain that I can be brought back to mobility with L-Dopa, I still feel so panicky when I'm very stiff that I'll take extra medication to avoid getting into or to lift myself out of the pit of despair. This super-fear is responsible for much of the adverse effect I and many others suffer from overdoses of medication. We would rather endure the discomfort and embarrassment of uncontrolled movements called dyskinesia, than risk the feeling akin to death that often accompanies extreme bradykinesia (slowness of movement) and akinesia (inability to move at all).

A second reason for great fear can be explained more simply. It is the thought that in case of an emergency, such as a fire, I would be unable to respond.

A third reason for fright was the discovery that my parkinsonism had advanced much more than I had realized. Apparently the medications and care I had been getting—and perhaps the momentum of living I had built up—had kept me going remarkably well considering what I now found my "baseline" to be.[2] I was afraid, therefore, that the new drug L-Dopa might not work as effectively for me as had the conventional drugs. If not, I thought I may never be able to get back to my recent functional level now that the momentum had been broken.

A fourth reason I lost my cool was the fear that my condition would upset my wife, children, other family, and friends and, of course, it did.

Furthermore, it was embarrassing to me to have anyone see me in a helpless state and for me to require their assistance in performing the most personal functions. Most of the nurses and nursing aides were so well trained and motivated that they put me at ease completely on this score. But it took only a few insensitive comments and actions to negate much of the confidence that had been built up so laboriously by the rest of the staff.

I remember two people, particularly, who undermined my morale. One was a male orderly who was supposed to help me with any personal task I couldn't do myself. He had seen me move about relatively well when I first entered the hospital and he didn't seem to understand why I couldn't continue to do so. He seemed to resent moving me in a wheel chair or helping dress me. And he vocally attributed my immobility to fear. "You are paralyzing yourself with fear," he commented. "You're scared stiff." And, of course, he was right. But his saying it only made me

---

[2]My basic condition probably was not as bad as it appeared to be immediately after withdrawal of Cogentin. Researchers have learned since then that "should a patient suddenly stop using an anticholinergic, often he will experience a rebound worsening effect. Because of this effect, these anticholinergics should never be withdrawn suddenly." (From a presentation by Dr. Harold L. Klawans at a symposium in San Diego, 6 November 1977, as summarized in *United Parkinson Foundation* 1977 *Newsletter*, no. 4, p. 1.)

more frightened. Further, it was the way he said it—
with a smile. The smile may have looked good to a
supervisor observing from a distance, but to me that
smile looked like a sadistic smirk.

My other tormentor was a night nurse who expressed her displeasure with all patients who rang the
call button for any reason. She gave the impression
that her main job was to type the daily report and any
interruption to help a patient was a gross imposition.
Because the patient load was small at the time, she was
often on duty alone, without the help of the aide to
which she was accustomed. Once my roommate, who
was too immobile to go to the bathroom, got uncomfortable waiting for a urinal. "What's keeping her?" he
moaned. "My bladder's about to burst."

"She's probably typing her report," I said. "She's
pretty slow at it."

"She's slow getting urinals, too. God, how I'd like
to pee on that report."

I sympathized with him, but my revenge fantasy was
different. I had an urge to punch her in the mouth. The
mouth that even said "Good morning" unpleasantly.

Fortunately, day follows night and the day nurses
were almost universally pleasant and helpful.

Most of the personnel in the Clinical Center seemed
to have special training, interest, and skills in dealing
with experimental patients. The head nurse was so
caring and so attentive that one of my visiting friends
said, "She acts as protective as a Jewish mother." Even
the cleaning personnel seemed to be well briefed on
our special needs and problems and they seemed
concerned about our welfare. The maid who had
regular duty in our wing, for example, kept up with the
progress or problems of each patient and she tried to
time her chores so that we would be least disturbed.

"I'll come back and vacuum later," she'd say if we were resting or listening to music. And she kept the rooms so clean that it added to my feelings of security.

I was overwhelmed with kindness. For example, once I was taken in a wheelchair to have my teeth cleaned as part of routine hospital procedure. The technician who did the cleaning noted how immobile I was and expressed great sympathy. She told me about a close relative of hers who also had Parkinson's. Using dental repair materials, the doctor had made large, custom-designed handles that enabled that relative to write, brush her teeth, and eat her meals more easily. She insisted on doing the same for me.

"But my situation is only temporary," I explained. "After I'm treated with L-Dopa, I hope I won't need such aids."

"I hope so, too," she said, "but in the meantime you could use some help. And if you get so much better that you don't need the special implements, we'll both be so happy we won't mind keeping them as souvenirs." Without further ado, she began taking wax impressions of my grip on a pen, a toothbrush, and a spoon. The next day I received from her three odd-looking but very useful tools. She had cemented a soupspoon and a toothbrush each into a large plastic tube, enabling me to grip and handle them more easily. She also gave me a gadget that attached to a pen. I don't remember its exact design, but I do remember that it enabled me to write much larger and faster than with a pen alone.

I still have the special spoon that enabled me to eat several meals I would otherwise have missed. I occasionally look at the odd device and think of the words of its creator after I said, "I wish I could repay your kindness."

"Just do something helpful for someone else when you get the chance. That's how I'd like to be repaid."

I feel indebted to scores of people, each of whom had some role in the enormous and complex team that was involved in my care, treatment, and research studies. The nurses were especially important in maintaining my morale. But, except for the chief clinical neurologist, the single staff member who gave me the most long-lasting help was the clinical social worker. He was regularly assigned to the wing where I stayed and made routine rounds with and without the medical doctors.

I believe that this procedure is far superior to the typical hospital policy of sending for a psychiatrist, psychologist, or social worker only when emergencies arise. Many patients are afraid or would be embarrassed to make a formal visit to anyone resembling a psychologist. Several times before and since my favorable experience with an on-the-spot counselor at NIH, I have been referred to a psychiatrist or psychologist for help in coping with anxiety, depression, or other problems. I almost always found some excuse to avoid going. But it was easy to accept the casual, informal, on-the-spot help provided by the NIMH psychiatric social worker. He happened to be highly qualified and skilled as a clinical social worker. And he needed all the skill he could muster to work with me and my family.

Fortunately, we had gotten acquainted informally and established a friendly relationship before I was taken off all my medications. A few days later, we went far beyond the casual get-acquainted stage.

When he appeared on his own rounds to visit patients, he found me flat on my back in bed, sobbing, and tears flowing profusely down my cheeks. At the

time I didn't even know exactly why I was crying. A
nurse had asked me why and I replied, "I just feel
miserable. And I can't do anything else."

"It's natural to feel depressed in your state," she
said, "but remember that you'll soon be getting better
and in the meantime you're lucky to have such a
wonderful wife and children and so many friends
visiting you. And the nursing staff will do all we can to
make you as comfortable as possible while you're
waiting for the new medication to work."

"I know, but. . ." I tried to respond. The tears,
however, interfered with my speech and I never finished the sentence. The nurse left after a reassuring
smile and a pat.

When the social worker appeared shortly thereafter
and tried to engage me in conversation, the emotional
outburst increased again the moment he made reference to my family. He tried to find out what was
bothering me, but I couldn't speak more than a few
words without breaking down emotionally. For the
first half hour or so he served, as he put it, "as a
shoulder to cry on." He didn't rush me or push me to
tell him what was bothering me. It took a few days for
me to sort out from the kaleidoscopic stream of
miseries those thoughts that were causing me the most
grief. At first, my counselor was mostly a listener, just
letting me pour it all out to a sympathetic ear. Then he
gradually began to ask questions that helped me identify my concerns.

After several discussions, I began to express my
feelings of depression largely in terms of regrets and
guilt feelings. I regretted not spending more time with
and not giving more attention to my wife and children
during my healthy years. I felt guilty because I had
worked so many hours beyond normal work days and

in addition had worn myself and my family down in order to earn my doctorate in education while continuing to work full time.

"I'm crying because I feel as if I've wasted the best years of my life and of my family and the sacrifices we made weren't worth it," I said. "Instead of getting a richer life to look forward to, all my family is getting is the prospect of an invalid to take care of. When I think of all the fun we could have had and didn't in order to get a worthless piece of sheepskin, I could kick myself around the block."

"What could you have done for fun?" the social worker asked.

"Well, family camping was one thing we all enjoyed greatly, so was travel, and sailing."

"Say, we've got something in common. Camping is my family's favorite recreation, too."

"Really? Where have you camped?"

"Well, actually," he hesitated, "we've only been on one real camping trip. That was when I finished a year of a Public Health Service assignment on an Indian reservation in New Mexico. I was gathering material for my doctoral dissertation—and we took a trip through the Southwest before we came home. We enjoyed the trip so much we've talked about another one but somehow haven't been able to manage it. Where have you camped?"

"Well, we began camping in 1955, when our two oldest were about five and four years old. I took a few weeks' vacation time before and after the NEA Convention, which was in Chicago then, and we had a great trip to places such as Tippicanoe State Park in Indiana, Lake Geneva, and Wisconsin Dells, Wisconsin. We camped for a few weeks most summers for the next ten years. We've been to Swallow Falls State Park and Deep Creek Lake in western Maryland several times, and that's about as good camping as we've found in the East. We also liked a place called Westmoreland State Park on the Potomac River, in Virginia. That's a place I'd highly recommend if you have only a week-end.

"Another place we enjoyed very much was Douthat State Park in Virginia," I went on, warming to my subject. "That's not far, yet it's in fairly high mountains, near a beautiful lake where you can swim and boat. But our kids remember it most because a friendly family next door invited us to a fireside party one night and taught us how to make jelly twists on a stick over a campfire. All you need are refrigerated biscuit dough, some margarine, and jelly. We make them often in our fireplace at home and relive our camping trips. We've got hundreds of color slides taken during our trips. I'd love to show you some of them."

Suddenly I realized that I had quit sobbing or even feeling sorry for myself and my voice was growing stronger.

"One of the most unusual places we camped in was Florida," I continued.

"I heard Florida campsites are infested with bugs and snakes," the social worker said.

"But not Highlands Hammock State Park, which is located on one of the few high spots in Florida and is quite different from the lower areas. They have a resident naturalist who conducts a jeep tour. You can see alligators, exotic birds, and all kinds of interesting plant life and never get a mosquito bite. You can also pick almost all the oranges and grapefruit you want."

My one-man audience glanced at his watch and said, "Say, Sid, I'd love to hear more about your camping experiences, and I hope you'll write down the names and some information about some of the best places you've been. But we've been talking for about an hour now, and I have another appointment I'm late for. I'll see you tomorrow. Until then, try to dwell on some of the fun things you've done rather than the things you missed. It sounds to me as if you've really been around. I wish I'd been to as many places with my family as you've been with yours."

The next day, when the social worker came on his rounds, he found me dry-eyed. I asked him more about his southwestern camping trip and his stay on the Navaho Indian Reservation.

"I'll give you an itinerary of our trip," he said, "so when L-Dopa enables you to camp again you can try some of the places. I'm sure your family would enjoy it."

Then he asked me what we'd been doing for family recreation since our last camping trip in 1965.

"Well," I told him, "in 1965 I bought a small sailboat, which had been a dream since childhood, a Sunfish, and taught my children to sail on nearby waters, such as the Potomac. And, we'd take it with us to accommodations we'd rent on lakes or bays such as Ocean City, or to the lakeside cottage of one of my wife's sisters in Worcester where we enjoyed staying several summers. This past year we splurged and took the whole family to a motel in Miami Beach during the winter vacation as well as to the Worcester cottage during the summer. I guess we've had more good times together than I realized before you stimulated me to talk about them."

"Have you and your wife ever taken a break from the children and gone away alone?" he asked.

"Not very often. Debbie is such a conscientious mother and she was always worried about leaving the children in someone else's care. Our parents lived too far away and were not well enough to babysit readily. Nevertheless, in 1952 we had a very enjoyable trip to my first NEA Convention. That was in Detroit. We had to cut it short because one of the children started crying so much it frightened my mother-in-law, who was taking care of her. We also went to Florida together one spring for a conference and had an enjoyable stay at the Carrilon, and we won a free week's vacation to a hotel in Minnesota in 1967. But our best trip was a week in Nassau in 1965 to celebrate completion of my doctorate."

"You're way ahead of me again," the social worker said. "In fact, I guess that you've spent much more time with your wife and children than most suburban fathers. I know many other men around here who work long hours or do advanced studies. And I know many others who spend time away from their families at bars, country clubs, liaisons with mistresses, or eyes glued to a TV set. I gather you don't do any of those things."

When I reflect on this social worker's skillful guidance, it occurs to me that I should have been immediately reassured, but such was not the case. Subconsciously I may have been considerably relieved: I didn't cry much anymore; however, this might also be attributed in part to the small amounts of L-Dopa I had begun taking. I believe the drug sometimes relieves one's depression before it relieves stiffness. At any rate I was not about to give up my guilt feelings yet. I started on a different tack.

"What you say is true," I said, "but I must be doing something wrong. I'm professionally trained as an educator and I've had some great successes in guiding and motivating all kinds of normal and problem kids, from the severely underprivileged in Harlem, New York, to the greatly overprivileged in Chevy Chase, Maryland. Yet, I seem to have little or no influence over my own children."

Since our younger son was the most openly rebellious and had recently been involved in some incidents that were particularly embarrassing and frustrating to my wife and me, I spoke at length about how he hated school with a passion; how he had tried to run away from home when he was five, and how when he was eleven he climbed out of his bedroom window late at night and had driven our automobile around. Although his early mental ability tests showed great potential, he refused to conform to school routines enough to learn even the fundamentals. School personnel labeled him "an underachiever," "immature," and "restless." He disrupted his classes, upset his teachers, and in the course of a brief conference frustrated a school psychologist to the point of tears. My wife and I had witnessed the latter incident and sympathized with the psychologist; we had had the same kind of experiences ourselves.

I wondered aloud to the social worker whether my illness or preoccupation with my work was a cause of David's worrisome behavior. I expressed particular concern also over how our youngest child's personality or attitude toward me might be affected, since Carol had not known me before I had symptoms of parkinsonism.

In regard to the latter point, I was somewhat reassured by the social worker's statement that if Carol didn't remember what I was like before parkinsonism affected me she probably was not very conscious that anything was seriously wrong.

"It's like the story about an acquaintance telling an

alcoholic, 'I didn't know you drank until I saw you sober one day.' Figuratively speaking, Carol has never seen you sober." The social worker's analysis was confirmed some years later by Carol herself who said, "I didn't think of you as sick. I didn't realize until I just read about it how much you and Mom suffered."

In regard to David, the social worker asked whether he evidenced any positive qualities.

"Indeed he does," I replied. "He's got phenomenal mechanical and manipulative skills. He can build or fix almost anything. And he has looks and personality that make him appealing to males and females alike of all ages."

After several such discussions, some of them with both Debbie and me, the social worker said, "Perhaps it's not David who's maladjusted. Perhaps society or the school is maladjusted, at least as far as David is concerned."

He urged us to quit worrying about David and our other children. "Try to enjoy your own lives as much as possible, and your satisfactions will automatically be picked up by your children," was a piece of advice he emphasized many times. It took many repetitions to make a dent on us. But delayed as our reaction may have been, we eventually tried to follow his counsel and had extremely gratifying results.

8 First Effects of Levodopa

All medications will be discontinued immediately on admission. . . Drug trials will not commence until two weeks thereafter.

Therapeutic Trial: A double-blind, cross-over study will be carried out to compare L-Dopa with an inert placebo. Both substances will be packaged in identical capsules and given in accordance with the same dose schedule. Each patient admitted to this study will be assigned a code number referable to his own drug supply. The order of Dopa or placebo administration will be at random and unknown to either the patient, his evaluators, or the ward staff. Provision will be made for drug cessation and/or code break if indicated for medical reasons. In the event of serious complication or side effect attributable to L-Dopa, treatment will be discontinued.

The above plans were part of the original protocol for the L-Dopa treatment I was to receive. The plan, however, was changed considerably in its application to me. The reasons illustrate how carefully NIH protects the health of experimental patients.

"When we saw how disabled and distressed you were after we took you off Cogentin," the neurologist told me several years afterward, "we decided to deviate from the protocol to avoid the possibility of causing you permanent harm. So we started L-Dopa after only one week of no medication instead of the two called for in the plan, and we gave up the double-

81

blind study entirely as far as you were concerned."

"But I remember being told that the medicine I was getting might be placebo or L-Dopa," I exclaimed.

"You did get some placebos," he explained. "But that was only to disguise the amount of L-Dopa you were getting as we gradually increased your daily dosage. If you were on a double-blind study, you would have a fifty-fifty chance of getting placebos or getting L-Dopa and neither you, the nurse who gave them to you, nor the physicians who observed you would know what you were getting. That's so expectations of what a drug will do won't influence the evaluation of it. If you don't know what you're getting, you don't know what to expect.

"But even though you were not originally part of a double-blind study, we learned a great deal from observing and testing you," he continued. "For example, the studies of your urine, blood, and spinal fluids provided basic information about what happens to a person taking L-Dopa. Since you were the first Parkinson patient at NIH to respond favorably to L-Dopa, what we learned from you helped us to test following patients and to design further experiments. We were interested in basic research on the *process* by which L-Dopa works and you served an important function in that research even though we focused primarily on treating you."

In reviewing the NIH records of that treatment, I've found that I was started on .5 grams of L-Dopa on February 28 and was gradually built up to a maximum of 8 grams on March 22. But I didn't know this at the time, so I anxiously prayed that I was receiving the real thing.

For the first few days, I couldn't tell at all whether I was getting any L-Dopa. But even the possibility seemed to make me feel better. The notes of my condition made by the nurses record that on March 1, only two days after starting L-Dopa, I "...was feeling better. Dressed before breakfast. Walked up and down hall. Felt that strength improved...." On March 2 a nurse noted "...Shuffling gait continues but posture better." By March 12 I started to feel really different in strange ways. I was restless and awoke from sleep that night at 1:00, 2:00 and 3:00 A.M. I finally got out of bed and stayed up most of the rest of the night. About the same time, I became easily aroused sexually. I also experienced increasing periods when I would walk and move my arms and hands more readily than during the previous weeks.

On March 13 I was feeling chipper enough to initiate what became known on the 2-West wing as the "chase the nurse game." One of the young nurses who noticed my increasing libido decided to use it to increase my motivation to exercise. She had been assigned the tedious task of accompanying me on one of my shuffling walks up and down the corridor. "Lift your feet. Take longer steps," were the constant reminders. But this playful nurse saved the exhortation simply by saying, "You're walking so well now, see if you can catch me. You can walk as fast as you want and take as big steps as possible, but no running allowed." She started off ahead of me, slowly at first, but she increased her pace as she heard me gaining on her. Warming to the chase and finding I could readily lift my feet, I stepped out so rapidly she had to run to keep ahead of me.

"I didn't say *I* wasn't allowed to run," she panted as we neared the end of the hall. I was wondering whether she would run into the closed door when the door opened and she ran instead right into the arms of her supervisor. After the two women untangled and straightened their caps a bit, the supervisor grinned and said to me, "Well, you must be among the two percent."

She was referring to a recently published report that strongly increased sexual desires are a side effect of L-Dopa, affecting about two percent of patients.

"I don't think so," I responded. "I've always been attracted to pretty nurses. My wife is a nurse and she can tell you I chased her before L-Dopa."

To myself I said, "Oh boy! I must really be on L-Dopa, not a placebo. And it seems to be working."

It kept working. The next morning when my wife came to visit I surprised, embarrassed, and pleased her with my new-found energy, mobility, and libido. Instead of stumbling around in the hall, I led her to my room, closed the door, tugged her down on my bed, and pulled the privacy curtain closed.

"Please," she gasped between kisses. "I'm glad you're feeling this much better, but they have rules against this in hospitals. Let's wait until you get home."

"To hell with the rules. We're married and it won't mess up their research."

"How do you know?" she stalled.

She didn't need to stall for long, for one luxury I didn't have at the Clinical Center was privacy. Every action or word that might have any significance was noted and recorded. "They even read your mind!" one of my roommates had declared.

I began to believe him after a nurse entered the room and, to my amazement, said: "How would you like a pass to go home for a few hours? Since you live so close to the Clinical Center, the doctor thinks it might be safe and helpful for you to get away from the hospital and see what home is like again."

My wife blushed. "That's a pleasant surprise."

The pass was issued from noon to 2:30. "Just enough time to enjoy a home-cooked meal and look around the house," said the doctor with a grin.

"Don't take time to cook," I urged my wife as she drove us home. "Some canned soup and a sandwich will be fine. In fact I'm not very hungry for food."

"And just think, the children are at school," Debbie said, as she, too, read my mind.

I still have a warm feeling when I recall the next two hours. We had lunch, I looked around the house, and we enjoyed sexual relations for the first time in months.

Debbie, too, wondered aloud whether L-Dopa had an aphrodisiac effect. I am still uncertain about this; but I believe that its effect on me and most other patients is like a general stimulant rather than a specific activator of sexual interest or activity. Reportedly, two percent of patients are affected sexually so strongly that it is equivalent to a harmful side effect, causing some to be taken off the medicine. However, I've never heard anyone admit to experiencing this effect.

My brief visit home seemed to have been so good for me that the next day I was issued another pass, this time for five hours, from 2:30 to 7:30 P.M. On that day I was on five grams of L-Dopa, still three grams away from the maximum of eight that I was to reach in six more days. Yet, although I was occasionally slow, stiff, and tremulous, I felt well enough part of the time at home to work in the backyard, clearing some of the debris out of the flower beds.

That was the day a friend who had previously seen

me in the hospital came to visit. Following is his description of how he perceived the dramatic effects of L-Dopa on me.

> When I first saw you in the hospital you were horrible. You looked like you were dead. You looked like a corpse. There was no muscle control at all. You were just lying there. You didn't seem to be able to move anything, except your eyes a little bit. Your speech was just barely audible and it was garbled. That was after they took you off your old medicines.
>
> The next time I saw you, after they had been giving you L-Dopa, it hadn't taken effect yet, and you were still in bad shape.
>
> A few days later the phone rang. It was you. You had a nice hearty voice! You were home! Natalie and I rushed over to your house and walked in and there you were running up and down the stairs like a little kid. You ran over and hugged Natalie and lifted her off the floor and you looked absolutely, completely normal. Every muscle was under control. I couldn't believe it. It was like a miracle.

My children, too, were pleasantly surprised as we had dinner together. I believe it was around this time that our youngest daughter, Carol, said: "You're almost perfect now. Will this medicine make you perfect?"

The next few days seemed to be pointing toward "perfection," but I never quite reached it. Although I was able to move about rather well most of the time, I still felt some rigidity and my movements were slow. Suddenly, during the late afternoon and early evening of the 21st of March, I experienced a feeling of relaxation and a surge of energy that freed, no, impelled me to walk briskly up and down the hall of the hospital ward. After calling my wife elatedly to report this new feeling, I sat down to write a note to my parents in New Jersey. To my own surprise, the letters

I formed were large and the pen moved so briskly that I filled about ten pages at one sitting. Were they surprised when they got my letter! The last communication had been a few sentences in cramped, wavering handwriting.

As soon as I finished the letter I felt compelled to walk about again. I paced up and down the hall so briskly that patients and nursing staff alike seemed to catch my excitement and they congratulated me upon my new-found mobility. I soon had an urge to explore more than the confines of the 2-West hallway, and so a nurse's aide was assigned to accompany me on a walk outside the "unit." She was somewhat nervous at first, since her last experience in walking with me was when I was very unsteady and I had often gotten down on one knee to get a new start for walking a few more steps. This time there was no need to assist me or catch me. Her main problem was keeping up with my pace. When we got back and we were asked where we had been, she replied, "All over the Clinical Center," and big as the Center is, she was almost correct.

By that time it was 11:00 P.M., but I was too excited to go to bed. I met the doctor in charge of the research program, who was still visiting patients, and shared my elation with him. The doctor's progress notes for that day record my improvement in objective medical terms. But they also note the first indications of what was to become a serious problem before long: the side effect of involuntary movements.

3/21 Patient now strikingly improved. Most evident is the decreased bradykinesia. Facial expression is normal, postural stability nearly normal, gait much improved (c̄ normal arm swing), finger tap now virtually normal bilaterally, handwriting speed increased many times, etc. Change in rigidity and tremor much less impressive. 1+ cogwheel rigidity persists in both arms and occasional mild, pill-rolling tremor breaks through at fingers bilaterally. Patient is elated to point of tears. Suggestion of toxic dyskinesia (? slight adventitious movement about mouth, involuntary head turning, ?? involuntary upward movements of both eyes) appeared briefly during late afternoon and early evening.

The next day my dosage of L-Dopa was increased from seven and one-half grams to eight grams, the maximum limit that had been predetermined as safe on the basis of the experimental work reported on a few score patients at other research centers up to that time. However, in addition to dyskinesia (uncontrolled movements), a new problem was noted in my medical record that day, "Difficulty getting to sleep." And so my dosage was reduced to seven and one-half grams the next day. This was the beginning of a seesawing back and forth, with the doctor increasing and decreasing my dosage. For a day or so after a change, the perfect balance sometimes seemed to be achieved; but then I would become under- or over-dosed. If I was underdosed, I would have periods of stiffness, slowness, tremor, or nervous feelings that I was about to experience stiffness. If overdosed, I would have involuntary movements of the head and facial muscles, and later of the arms. And even when underdosed, I continued to have difficulty sleeping for more than a few hours at a time.

Recently, in a conversation with the physician who had been in charge of the L-Dopa experiment, he said: "You know, we made some mistakes on you. We've learned a lot since. And patients who come down with the disease now are more fortunate than you were, just as you were more fortunate than those who needed treatment even a year earlier."

Apparently, one of the mistakes they made was to build up the dosage of L-Dopa too rapidly. I have heard several expert neurologists say that when the dosage is increased at a rate much slower than the rate at which it was given to me there is less likelihood of getting dyskinesia, or at least that side effect takes longer to develop.

At the time, however, the rate at which my dosage was increased was considered to be quite slow and side effects seemed negligible compared to the improvement in my condition.

On March 26 I started going to work at my office, first for only part of the day, and returning to be observed and to sleep at the NIH Clinical Center each evening. Then I was occasionally allowed to go home. As soon as it seemed safe to do so, I was discharged from the Clinical Center with arrangements to be seen at weekly intervals as an outpatient by the same neurologist who had initiated the Dopa research program.

The date of discharge was April 7. The cherry trees were in bloom, the sun shone brightly, and warm spring breezes carried promises of even better days ahead.

The summary of my hospital stay, written by the physician who gave me a thorough physical exam upon discharge, was likewise all sunny. The summary mentioned only two side effects from L-Dopa that I had experienced. One was a drop in white blood cell count which came back to the normal range and "only a very slight and transient gastric distress during the course of his therapy." The report went on to say: "He had a very remarkable and dramatic improvement in his Parkinson symptoms with relaxation of his rigidity and bradykinesia. At the time of his discharge he was on eight grams of L-Dopa per day. He had returned to work, was feeling quite well and was very pleased with his progress."

Indeed I was pleased. I felt as if I had a new lease on life and I was determined to make the most of it.

9 The Prize and the Price

FOR SEVERAL MONTHS after L-Dopa alleviated my symptoms, many other people echoed Carol's observation that I appeared to be "almost perfect." Some even assumed that I had been cured of my ailment, and most expected me to function normally. This reaction pleased and reassured me so much that I was almost convinced that I was as good as new. I had many happy experiences to encourage this feeling but I also had many reminders that L-Dopa exacts a high price in side effects and in demands on lifestyle. Considering the prize, however, the price seemed well worth paying.

Before L-Dopa worked its magic, for example, family mealtimes were usually very strained periods for everyone present. I ate with difficulty and responded to questions and comments with grunts or monosyllables, if at all. One of the first evenings after L-Dopa my wife exclaimed, "Welcome back to the living!" I don't remember what the talk was about, but I do remember the thrill of being able to eat with such ease that I could also listen to the conversation and find time, energy, and voice to respond.

My stored-up words poured forth in such torrents that my wife and children competed for a chance to talk. They—my wife especially—had been frustrated for years by sporadic communication with me. Now they came on so strong that I sometimes felt overwhelmed and resorted to withdrawing again. At work I had somewhat similar experiences. Colleagues who had saved up problems and projects while I was "dragging my anchor" at the office or was receiving treatment at NIH now came forth with requests for action. And I was eager to act. I undertook the largest publishing project of my career, requiring a sizeable budget appropriation that I confidently assured our officers would be recovered through sales.

Another great source of satisfaction was playing golf, for golf, I knew, tested to the utmost the nervous and muscular controls that parkinsonism deteriorated. Before L-Dopa, golf had been my favorite sport. I had tried to play even after my symptoms had advanced so far that I could barely walk around the course. The season before I started on L-Dopa I was so embarrassed by my erratic swing that I sought out one of the worst courses in the Washington area because it was the least crowded. It seemed to be frequented by old-timers, heavy drinkers, and other types of duffers, so I didn't think I'd be as conspicuous as on some of the better courses.

Most people politely ignored my feeble efforts. But the last time I played before I became an experimental patient at NIH, I knew by the shake of his head that the starter noticed me at the first tee. I had approached the ball with a quivering club and swung stiffly at it three times before making a timid contact that dribbled the ball about fifty yards down the fairway.

A few months later, after L-Dopa and after I'd once again enjoyed the thrill of hitting straight two-hundred yard drives at a golf range, I returned to the same golf course. I was assigned to fill out a foursome of semi-inebriated duffers. Triumphantly my first drive clicked, swished, and dropped neatly right at the edge of the green. I wondered whether the starter had noticed. When I returned to the starting point to check in for the second nine, I found that he had indeed remembered. He came close to me and said in a low, confidential tone, "You sure are playing better since you quit drinking."

When my son, David, heard that story, he invited me to play with him on a better and busier golf course. That game didn't go quite as well. The pressure to keep up with better players caused me to tighten-up and my score was much less impressive than the one I had made at "duffer's heaven." By the time we played nine holes, I was completely exhausted. Nevertheless, I did well enough to cause David to report to his mother, "It was fun playing with Dad. What a difference from last year. That was a drag."

As I successfully resumed other ordinary activities, such as driving my turn in the car pool, talking on the telephone, going out to the theater or movies at night, or helping entertain dinner guests at our home, I vowed that I would never again take for granted the joy of being able to do such ordinary things.

My euphoria, however, was frequently replaced with temporary discouragement or even despair. For although externally I often appeared to be acting fairly normally, I usually had vague feelings of discomfort— internal pressures, fogginess, restlessness, sleepiness, or overstimulation. The effect of the medication was very uneven. Each time I took L-Dopa I went through a cycle ranging from stiffness, slowness, and sometimes tremor, to overstimulation and possibly uncontrollable movements of the facial muscles, head, or trunk. Since I took medication every two waking hours, this cycle occurred about eight times a day.

I rarely got adequate rest at night because the drug overstimulated me when it was still in my bloodstream and after it wore off I would get so stiff I would awaken in the middle of the night. Another reason for waking was that L-Dopa acts as a diuretic. I had to go to the bathroom at least once or more each night, a need made more urgent by the complication of an enlarged prostate. But I was usually too stiff to walk to the bathroom, so I kept medicine and water at my bedside and waited until the L-Dopa made me mobile enough to move about. I could not loosen up just by lying there, however; I had to stretch and exercise to become mobile.

At the time my wife and I shared a double bed, so my movements disturbed her sleep. I then took to crawling to the bathroom and sitting there, occasionally exercising as much as I could until I loosened up. By that time I was wide awake and overstimulated so I walked about the house until I got tired enough to go back to bed. Whereas I had been accustomed to eight hours, I now got only a few hours of sleep at a time and a total of five or six hours a night. Cumulative fatigue became a major problem.

My muscles always seemed to be tense, even when I was able to control them. The neurologist, who continued to see me frequently as an outpatient, told me that a minimum of five hours of continuous sleep or bed rest was necessary to maintain good muscle tone. He urged me to try to stay down even if I awoke, but I found it almost impossible to remain relaxed once I woke up. I had a compulsion to move about, and if I found that I couldn't an overwhelming fear would develop. I would gulp down an L-Dopa pill in desperate efforts to get mobile again. Even though my regular medication schedule called for only one dose a

night, I sometimes took two. And the more medication I took at night the more difficulties I had the next
day. It seemed that my body needed a rest from
medication during sleeping hours in order for it to
work reliably during the day. This premise seemed to
be proven a few years later when I finally did get to
sleep five or more continuous hours a night and felt
much better the next day.

But at the time I first went on L-Dopa my physician
was reluctant to prescribe a sleeping pill and I was
reluctant to take one. We both thought my body had
to cope with a heavy load of toxic medication already.
So we concentrated on "natural" methods of getting a
good night's sleep. Some of the techniques that seemed
to work best for me were the standard ones of relaxing
exercise (preferably a long walk outdoors in the evening), warm milk before bedtime, a warm bath, and
avoidance of talking or thinking about problems before going to sleep. All these helped some but were not
enough to give me adequate rest each night. So I
napped during the day when I was able to do so.
Napping, however, upset my delicate chemical balance, usually causing either stiffness or the opposite
extreme of involuntary movements. I soon found that
the effect of L-Dopa was very sensitive to a number of
factors in addition to rest. Among the most important
are exercise, diet, and emotions.

Variations in any of these may cause a need for
variation of dosage of medication in order to maintain
optimum balance. The amount and timing of medication worked out by the doctors fit my average regimen
at the time I was under observation in the hospital.
After I was discharged, however, I found that vigorous
or extended exercise "uses up" the medication more
rapidly than moderate activity, and that inactivity

doesn't stimulate the nerves, muscles, or circulation enough to make optimum use of the L-Dopa. In either case, I would become underdosed—that is, stiff and immobile.

I recall demonstrating the effect of exercise very dramatically to my neurologist at NIH when I arrived in a dyskinetic state for an outpatient check-up visit. My head and arms were moving involuntarily. "Give me ten minutes and I'll be normal," I told the doctor. I then went out and walked quickly up the stairs from the second floor to the twelfth floor and back again. When I returned, I was a bit out of breath but I had no involuntary movements.

Over a long period of time I've learned to estimate about how much exercise I need to keep a good balance with my basic prescribed dosage. In the early months on L-Dopa, it seemed relatively easy to work off an overdosage, but as the cumulative effects of the medication caused longer and more intense periods of dyskinesia, it became increasingly difficult to eliminate the involuntary movements once they had begun. I found that prevention is the best cure. If I exercise *before* the medication has a chance to reach its peak, I can often avoid the effects of overdosage. An early morning walk is almost essential to my well-being during the rest of the day.

But exercise is only one of several variables affecting the action of L-Dopa. Diet is extremely important but still inadequately understood. A few facts, however, have been scientifically established. Protein and vitamin B^6, for example, have been found to interfere with the action of L-Dopa.

Interestingly, with interpretative help from NIH staff, I discovered both of these phenomena through my own experiences and observations before there were any published reports from research. At the request of the clinical investigator, I had been keeping a log, recording when I took my medication, how much I took, what my condition was at different times of the day—that is, was I nearly normal, stiff, or over-stimulated?—and any other occurrences that I thought might be affecting my condition. After a few months, certain patterns emerged. I noted that I was most frequently stiff in the early and middle afternoon and the early and middle evening. By late afternoon and late evening I usually loosened up and became mobile. This was not an absolute pattern, however. I tried to think about what was different about the afternoons and evenings that I didn't become stiff. It slowly became apparent that they were days when I had eaten light lunches or dinners. Then I began to keep track of what I ate and how I felt afterward.

When my written observations indicated that I invariably got stiff if I ate a meal with a great deal of meat, I thought that protein might be the culprit. I soon felt reasonably certain that this was the case and reported it to the NIH neurologist. I thought he would dismiss my theory out of hand because earlier he had shown little interest in diet as a factor. To my surprise, he commended me for my observation, saying he had recently read a paper by Dr. Cotzias and associates reporting that in some of their experimental patients, high protein diets had been found to interfere with the effectiveness of L-Dopa. When these patients were switched to low-protein diets, their conditions im-proved; some were able to manage with less medica-tion.

By trial and error over a long period of time, I was able to determine about how much protein per meal or snack I could tolerate without serious interference with the medication. With the help of the Clinical Center dietician I identified this amount to be about eight grams of protein such as cheese, beef, or nuts. I found that eight ounces of milk had about the same effect.

But it wasn't just protein that interfered with the action of L-Dopa. I found a similar effect from sweet potatoes, bananas, and raisins. And a portion of beef containing the same amount of protein as portions of chicken or fish blocked the action of L-Dopa more than the latter foods.

After reporting these observations, I was told that the foods causing the problem are rich in vitamin B[6], which tended to block the use by the brain of L-Dopa. The dietician gave me a list of foods high in B[6]. The doctor, however, cautioned me to moderate my intake of B[6] but not to eliminate it, for it is very important to one's health.[1]

And so began a painstaking effort by my wife and me to balance my meals and snacks. Debbie bought a sensitive kitchen scale on which she weighed each of my protein snacks and portions of protein going into main meals. Since I ate a snack with each dose of medication, this meant weighing at least eight portions of food a day. It seemed like a great deal of trouble to go to—and it was—but it helped me keep more evenly balanced than I would have been otherwise. We found that out on the occasions when travel or other factors prevented the careful control of food intake.

And so my wife and I spent much time and effort balancing exercise, rest, and food. Like circus jugglers we learned to control those three factors almost auto-

---

[1]Later it was found that B[6] does *not* usually interfere with L-Dopa when the drug is given in combination with a decarboxylase inhibitor, such as carbidopa. Carbidopa inhibits parts of the body other than the brain from absorbing L-Dopa.

matically. But an important fourth influence on parkinsonism—emotions—proved to be less controllable or predictable.

One day at work, I became so engrossed in a filmstrip I was reviewing that I was twenty minutes late in taking a dose of medication. Until I noticed the time, I had been talking and moving with no problems. But after I realized I was late in taking my medication, I got so panicky my hand shook as I got out the capsules and I was barely able to handle the glass of water to wash them down.

One of my colleagues present who was familiar with my dependence on the "magic pills" remarked: "Are you sure this illness isn't psychological? I've seen your symptoms disappear before when you were doing something interesting and I've seen you start to shake and get stiff when you're frustrated or tense."

"If you mean that parkinsonism is *caused* by psychological or emotional factors," I told him, "medical research and my own experiences indicate that's not true. The basic cause is physical, or more precisely, a chemical imbalance; but psychological and emotional factors seem to have a very great influence on how that chemical imbalance affects a person and even on how well he responds to medication. I believe that given two people with similar degrees of physical or chemical deterioration causing parkinsonism, their feelings of well being and their abilities to function can vary greatly according to emotional and psychological factors that affect them."

"Of course that's true with any illness and of people who aren't ill at all," my colleague responded.

"Yes, but with people who have Parkinson's, psychological factors are even more important. Perhaps it's because we're so delicately balanced that the slightest push can knock us flat."

At that point I felt so flat myself, we terminated the conversation and I had to rest for almost half an hour before the medication helped me resume work. But that conversation helped sharpen my observation of the many ways in which emotional and psychological factors affect me and other parkinsonians.

Probably the most important emotional factor in overcoming illness is the sense of well being and security that comes from being loved. This phenomenon has been expressed in many ways. Nurses speak of the therapeutic effects of TLC (tender loving care). Dr. Oliver Sacks writes ". . . . Love is the *alpha* and *omega* of being; and . . . the work of healing, or rendering whole is, first and last, the business of love."[2]

I have been fortunate enough to have enjoyed the healing effects of love in its broadest definition: wifely love that put a smile on Debbie's face when she was crying inside; children's love, which caused a son to threaten (out of my sight) to knock a boy's block off for laughing at my strange movements; love of friends and relatives who kept inviting me back to dinner even though I tipped the wine over and dropped food on the floor; the love of colleagues at work, who cheerfully picked up loads I couldn't carry; the TLC I received from dedicated and humane nursing and medical personnel; and, underlying all, the unstinting motherly and, to a lesser degree, fatherly love throughout my childhood that caused me to *expect* to find love, success, and security in the rest of the world for the balance of my life. There are some advantages to having an old fashioned "Jewish mother."

---

[2]Oliver Sacks, *Awakenings* (Garden City, NY: Doubleday & Co., 1974), p. 234.

One often finds what one expects to find, and I am a persistent optimist. Even during the frightening days when I was almost immobilized because of the withdrawal of all medication, I was able much of the time to maintain a positive outlook because I *expected* my condition to improve.

And when, after it did improve, but the involuntary movements and uneven effects of L-Dopa began to wear me down, I had confidence that research would come up with an improvement in medication to help me. And it did.

10 Rewards of Being a Pioneer Patient

ABOUT A YEAR after starting on L-Dopa, I agreed to reenter the hospital for adjustment of my treatment.

The results of my second stay in the Clinical Center were not nearly as dramatic as the first effects of L-Dopa a year earlier. But in long-term value to myself and to the advance of medical research, they were probably more important. Between admission as an "inpatient" on January 12 and discharge March 31, 1970, I became the first experimental patient at NIH to successfully add MK-485 to L-Dopa.

In the fall of 1970, I switched to MK-486, a refined version of MK-485, now called carbidopa, which was later combined with L-Dopa in one pill to make Sinemet, which for several years has been the preferred anti-Parkinson medication.

As mentioned earlier, the great contribution of carbidopa is to reduce the amount of L-Dopa required for treatment and to make its effects more consistent. It does this by inhibiting the chemical breakdown of L-Dopa by parts of the body other than the brain. Since the brain is the only organ where L-Dopa works to alleviate the symptoms of parkinsonism, carbidopa reduces the amount of L-Dopa needed by about 70-80 percent. For example, my daily intake of L-Dopa was reduced from 7500 mg a day to about 1500 mg plus 125 mg of MK-486 a day. Thus, my body had to endure only about one-fifth as much toxic effect from L-Dopa, which over a long period of time could have very harmful effects.

Carbidopa itself has hardly any side effects or toxicity. Thus, when I left the hospital in March of 1970, my feeling of well being was considerably improved. The reduction of the L-Dopa dosage practically eliminated problems of what my medical reports referred to as "gastro-intestinal (GI) distress," and I experienced fewer episodes of stiffness and tremor. The problem of involuntary movements remained but was usually mild enough to tolerate.

At times, though, the dyskinesia was so extreme that I felt as if I was spinning in a centrifuge. My arms and legs seemed to be pulling from their sockets, my inner organs seemed to be pressing to get outside my body or to turn themselves inside out. My muscles, particularly in my arms and around my shoulders, developed very sharp pains and cramps.

The dyskinesia could be almost entirely eliminated by reducing the dosage of medication to the point of slight underdose, but underdosage was so disabling, depressing, and frightening that I preferred to be slightly overdosed even at the cost of involuntary movements and the knowledge that overdosage might, over the long term, cause permanent damage to my body. It's a risk I'm willing to take in order to live a reasonably full life now.

I've often been helped over difficult emotional periods by reflecting on my role as a pioneer experimental patient in development of a medication that is helping thousands of fellow victims of parkinsonism. This satisfaction is enhanced by my recent discovery of the significance of some of the incidental basic research studies that were conducted on me while I was hospitalized six different times between 1970 and 1973. During these admissions—some for only a few days, some for a few months—I earned my keep as a guinea pig. While I was at NIH to try new medications or for observation or treatment of parkinsonism or related ailments, I provided data for literally scores of studies, ranging from analysis of blood, urine, and spinal fluid to the effects of L-Dopa on brain waves, blood pressure, and intellectual and memory function.

During these few years, I estimate that I contributed hundreds of gallons of urine, dozens of quarts of blood, and a few pints of spinal fluid to the NIH laboratories—all taken under special conditions designed to add to the basic information about the mechanisms of parkinsonism, the drugs used to treat it, and the reactions of the body to both.

Some of this information has been of direct help to me; some has led to improved treatment for parkinsonism over a long, sometimes indirect route; some has helped make discoveries that will be useful in treating other ailments, such as mental illness; and some are just there, part of the pool of scientific knowledge, facts which may lead nowhere, or which some day—a month or a century from now—may help make a major new breakthrough in medical treatment.

For example, I was told recently by an NIH research administrator that one of the studies most unpleasant and difficult for me to endure in 1971 has helped lead to improved combinations of medications to produce more even responses to treatment of parkinsonism. The experiment was designed to compare patient response to L-Dopa and MK-486 administered orally to the response when the medications were infused intravenously at a constant rate.

During each of two days involved, I had to fast and

lie still and flat on my back for about eight hours. This may not seem to be difficult, but at the time I would experience strong compulsions to get up and move about frequently. In addition, during the intravenous infusion I had the discomfort and trauma of a tube attached to my right arm through which the medication was infused and a needle and plastic "tap" inserted in my left arm which was used to draw blood samples every fifteen minutes. Thus, I could not move either arm without incurring injury.

This experience was so frightening at the time that I still sweat a little when I recall it. I remember imagining that I was in a straitjacket. And several times during the day I felt that I just couldn't stay down any longer. I was able to make it through the day only with the constant distraction of a pleasant doctor conducting the study and the TLC of the nurses in attendance. But as soon as the ordeal was over, I was proud and pleased that I had sweated it out.

From the point of view of the researchers, the important outcome of this experiment, which was conducted on a few other patient volunteers, is the knowledge that the "on-off" effect can be controlled or corrected. The knowledge of this fact helps me personally by giving me hope that the researchers will come up with improved treatment. It also confirms and adds to my ideas on how I could help myself immediately to reduce the "on-off" effect by adjusting my own routines of living.

The study proved by the analysis of frequent samples of blood that when L-Dopa is administered orally every two and one-half hours, the amount of the drug in the bloodstream varies greatly between doses. When the levels of levodopa in the bloodstream were at their peak, periods of maximum suppression of parkinsonism and the appearance of drug-induced uncontrolled movements (dyskinesia) generally followed, while low levels of dopa in the bloodstream were followed by the return of severe parkinsonism and the disappearance of dyskinesia.

On the other hand when infusion kept the level of dopa in the bloodstream at a constant level, the "on-off" effect was eliminated. This was evident to me while the study was being made. I was hardly under- or overdosed all day. An exception was when I sat up briefly for urgent reasons. Then the extra effort required more medication to eliminate stiffness or tremor. Another interesting outcome was the demonstration that strong emotional moods brought on by discussing sensitive topics also affected Parkinson symptoms. Talking about depressing thoughts caused me to feel stiffness and tremor, and discussion of especially pleasant, relaxing, or exciting matters caused me to have dyskinesia, even though neither my dosage of medication nor body position had changed.

It is, of course, impractical to inject medication into one's veins at a constant rate all day long or to keep variable conditions such as activity or emotions constant. But the newly confirmed knowledge stimulated other ideas for achieving more even effects from L-Dopa.

The researchers first thought the answer lay in a "sustained release" capsule such as is used for a popular patent medicine cold remedy. The theory was that different coatings and different size particles of medication in each capsule would be designed to release the medication at rates which would maintain a constant level of dopa in the bloodstream. Another presumed benefit from the time-release capsule would be a less frequent need to take medication.

Theoretically, this sounded so logical it seemed "only a matter of time and money before an effective time-release capsule will be developed," one of the researchers told me. But as I found out personally some months later, when I volunteered to try a time-release capsule, there were a few catches.

The basic problem is that the rate of release of the medication depends upon such variable conditions as body temperature, chemical composition of the fluids in the digestive tract, the rate and nature of metabolism of each individual, intake of food and drink, amount of activity, and other factors, known and unknown, that can't very well be predicted or controlled by pharmacists or doctors. Incidentally, it was found that even the cold remedy that provided the inspiration for time-release L-Dopa is not released at a constant rate: Variation in dosage is not as noticeable or crucial, however, since the medication does not have as powerful or critical an effect on the body as L-Dopa.

After unsuccessful trials of several versions of time-release L-Dopa at NIH and elsewhere, researchers turned to other ways of reducing the "on-off" effect. Armed with basic information through studies of blood, urine, spinal fluid, and observation of patient behavior in the time-release and other studies, reduction in "on-off" effect has been achieved for some patients. This has been accomplished through reduction or re-timing of dosage of L-Dopa or Sinemet, development of new drugs such as bromocriptine, and the combination of more than one drug timed so that one will provide more help while the level of the other is at a low point in its cycle. Although considerable progress has been made, discovery of the optimum drug or combination is still around the corner. Still,

the finding from the intravenous infusion experiment
that elimination of the "on-off" effect is theoretically
possible gives me hope that the corner will be turned
soon. While the medical researchers are trying to
develop new medications, I am trying to improve my
own response to existing drugs.

My earlier trial-and-error efforts to control diet,
exercise, rest, and emotional factors were refined by
more specific knowledge of how the drugs work,
gained from the studies in which I myself was a
subject.

Studying the charts showing the peaks and ebbs of
concentration of dopa in the blood impressed me with
the need to time my most vigorous activities for the
peak period and the least demanding for times when
there was little medication in my blood.

Since the study I was in indicated that my absorp-
tion of L-Dopa was even shorter than the average
patient's cycle of two and one-half hours, I usually
could count on only about three-quarters of an hour
to an hour per cycle when I was able to function
actively. Thus, I often left a TV program or book at
the most interesting point in order to get a walk in
before bedtime or was reduced to watching a dull
program because I couldn't function well enough at
the time to do anything else.

One of my most difficult adjustments was the
timing of conferences at work and conversations with
my family or friends. There were times when I would
become involved in an important discussion during a
low point in my cycle. Starting out slowly and calmly,
I would get more and more excited and restless as the
drug reached peak concentration. Then I had to make
the difficult choice of interrupting the conversation in
order to walk off the peak of muscle stimulation or

continue the discussion with the probable result of severe dyskinesia. Once dyskinetic I would become too uncoordinated to walk and would later slip into the trough of underdosage without being able to get the needed exercise.

Even though I knew what would happen, I sometimes stayed to try to finish a conversation because it was disconcerting both to me and others to continually break off discussions. But when I did persist, another problem arose. With the physical dyskinesia, which was distracting enough to the other person or persons, came a sort of mental dyskinesia. I found it difficult to concentrate or stay with a subject for long. I would interrupt the other person or even myself in the middle of a sentence. This problem was particularly difficult to handle on the telephone because I couldn't hold the phone firmly due to the dyskinsesia, and my frustrating efforts to do so made my voice and thoughts waver even more than in a face-to-face conversation. The resulting odd sounds often frightened the person at the other end of the line.

I've written the above in the past tense partly because I've learned more precisely what the cycles are and how to accommodate to them better, so that I time my conversations and calls as much as I can to fit my optimum periods.

Sexual relations presented the greatest challenge to timing. My peak period of mobility was so short that if I started to get amorous toward the end of the drug cycle, I would run out of energy at a most crucial point in the lovemaking cycle. It didn't increase Debbie's libido for me to say, "Excuse me, I've got to take my pills now," and wait half an hour before continuing. She would usually fall asleep before the half hour was up. So I tried to time our lovemaking to begin shortly after I had taken my medication and at times of the day when we were least tired.

Adjusting to the drug cycle is one more example of the key to coping with parkinsonism—accommodation. The person who expects to carry on a perfectly normal life because he is taking a helpful drug such as Sinemet is doomed to frustration. But if you are willing to accommodate to the realities of the illness and the treatment you stand a much better chance of leading a satisfying, even enjoyable life.

It took me a long time to accept that simple concept and I am still in the process of applying it.

11 Seeking the Impossible

DESPITE THE TRIBULATIONS I endured during the six years between 1965, when parkinsonism first became a serious problem, and 1971, when it became almost intolerable, I resisted accommodation to limitations imposed by the ailment. Instead, I tried desperately, in the words of Dr. Oliver Sacks, ". . .to transcend the possible, to deny its limits and to seek the impossible. . ."[1] That is, I tried to conduct my life as if I were not ill. My efforts to transcend the impossible resulted in a vicious cycle. The more I ignored my limitations, the greater those limitations became.

But between 1971 and 1973, I hit new lows: physically, mentally, and in key human relationships that eventually forced me to accommodate to reality—to adjust the style of my life to the conditions of my life.

I was pushed deeper into the valley of despair by pressures at home and at work. At home my wife's buoyant spirit and emotional support weakened as she herself became overwhelmed with problems. About that time her period of menopause began, bringing with it physical discomfort, emotional upset, and depression. I have known women to have been pushed into depression by any one of the problems Debbie faced: adjusting to four independent-minded, adult and teenage children; living with a husband whose

[1]Oliver Sacks, *Awakenings* (Garden City, NY: Doubleday & Co., 1974), p. 226.

111

frustrating, mysterious illness often made him seem a frightening stranger; and experiencing the trauma of a difficult menopause. Yet most of the time Debbie was able to cope with all three situations at once. Friends and relatives, and even her own children, hardly ever saw her lose her cool.

"Mom made us feel that you had an ideal husband-wife relationship and that your illness was not a very serious problem. I didn't even know she was in menopause until it was almost over," one of my children told me afterward.

But while Debbie appeared to be laughing on the outside, she was sometimes bitterly crying on the inside. The intensity of her grief and her frustration concerning my illness were explained a few years later. She recalled that one of the most frustrating problems was my withdrawal from guiding or even communicating with our children and my difficulty in communicating with her. "When I wanted to talk," she said, "I had to wait until the time was right. . . I remember walking out to the back yard thinking if I could only scream, I would. I just had half a scream caught in my throat a lot of the time. I learned to live in pieces."

She usually tried to shield me from the depths of her grief and depression. But her feelings came through to me—in the tone of her voice, the way she looked at me or avoided looking at me, the way she touched me or avoided touching me, and sometimes in direct statements.

It was during this period that we changed from sleeping together in a double bed to sleeping in separate beds. Perhaps it doesn't seem so serious for husband and wife to sleep in separate beds. Many spouses do it all their lives. But Debbie and I were lonely, isolated, and frightened by the separation.

After nearly twenty-five years of togetherness, each of us came to feel rejected by the other. How then did it happen, and why didn't we remedy the situation when we became aware of its implications? Partly because the situation grew slowly and unplanned and partly because it was accompanied by emotional crises that were too strong to overcome.

I previously described the problem of restless nights. At first I used to return to bed, but as the problem continued I found it increasingly difficult to get back to sleep. I was plagued with fears and restlessness, especially in the dark. Debbie was a light sleeper and my tossing and turning disturbed her. We both sought the security of sleeping in each other's arms, but my compulsion to move was too frequent for her to be comfortable.

After a few months of such restless nights, I took to finishing the last few hours of the night in an empty bed or couch where I could put the light on, read, listen to the radio, or watch television to distract me from my fears. During this period, I found that darkness increased my depression and anxiety. After tossing and turning in the dark, I would often fall asleep with a bright light shining in my face. Or, I'd drop off to sleep as soon as the morning sun pushed reassuring rays of light around the edges of the window shades.

Thus, in the course of my restless nights I'd sometimes sleep in three different beds. It seemed a waste of effort for Debbie to have all that extra linen to wash and beds to make. In addition, the noise of my rattling around from one room to another disturbed not only Debbie's sleep but that of the two children still at home. And so we decided that I'd sleep in a separate room.

It had its advantages in that I could set it up for my

convenience with TV, radio, lights, water, and urinal handy. At first it seemed to be a better arrangement. But soon the loneliness set in, for both my wife and me.

The physical separation seemed to carry over emotionally as well. We became more critical of each other, more short-tempered. My emotional condition was no doubt also affected considerably by the long-term side effects of levodopa, which can cause "mental changes including paranoid ideation and psychotic episodes, depression . . . and 'dementia.' "[2]

By February 1973 I had become so emotionally unstable that I would fly into rages upon slight provocation. Despite my wife's tremendous patience and support over a period of years, as my frustrations grew I would blame her for not being sensitive enough.

Between 1971 and 1973, I found it increasingly difficult to concentrate for long periods of time or to make decisions. It was difficult to tell whether my illness, the side effects of the medication, or emotional reactions to life's problems were responsible.

At work, I found dealing with personnel problems and changing organizational and operational conditions increasingly difficult. When asked to draw up a reorganization plan for the publishing function of the organization, I reorganized myself, with the approval of my supervisor, into a consultative position entailing hardly any administrative responsibility.

There was clearly less pressure in the new position and no reduction in salary. For awhile my spirits and physical condition were obviously buoyed. But after a few months, the physical problems of the work day seemed to be overwhelming again. If I remem-

---

[2]*Physician's Desk Reference*, 30th ed., s.v. "Levodopa."

bered to take my medication on time, got exercise at the right time, ate on schedule and just the right foods and quantities, took a few rests during the day, and didn't have much frustration or pressure, I might have a fairly productive day. But all these things are difficult to manage in a work situation.

The most difficult part was getting to and from the office. The twelve-mile drive became too much for me, or too scary for my car pool associates, and so when my turn came someone else drove. But then a new problem arose. I would often have difficulty walking out to the car or getting from the parking garage to my office. I could sometimes make it only by running. A friend would go ahead of me to clear the way, or follow carrying my briefcase. I was fortunate to have such good and patient friends. Some days they would wait for me because I could not make it to the auto and had to rest or wait for my medication to work. When I had such a bad day that I felt I had to see the doctor on an emergency basis, or just couldn't bear to be at the office any longer, they would take me home early.

During those difficult days, I often took what I called an emergency dose of medicine to enable me to function. These emergency doses became more and more frequent and more damaging in their side effects. Also, to keep from giving up during that difficult period I resorted to an "if only" philosophy:

"If only the researchers come up with an improved medication."

"If only our children wouldn't pose so many problems."

"If only I could sleep through the night."

"If only I could live closer to work."

After awhile it seemed that the last hope was the only one I could accomplish. One day, while as-

sembling a canopy bed for our daughter Ellen, I told
Debbie about my desire to live closer to work. It was
typical of my communications with her at this time
that I blurted out my news without adequate preparation or discussion. Her immediate reaction was: "We
should at least wait until Carol finishes high school. It
would be bad for her to move now."

This reaction triggered a rage that surprised me as
well as Debbie. "Bad for her!" I screamed. "Won't it
be worse if I crack up?" In my anger I began to swing a
post for the bed canopy at the other posts on the bed.
After I had cracked a few posts, Debbie pleaded with
me to stop.

"Hit me, if you're angry at me. Don't take it out on
Ellen's bed."

And to the shock of both of us, I did hit her. I
slapped her on the face—the only time in our thirty
years together that I ever struck her.

Suddenly, we had run out of "if onlys."

"We'd better see if the doctors at NIH can do
anything for me," I said.

Within two hours I was, once again, a patient at the
NIH Clinical Center. I agreed to participate in a few
experimental procedures, including trial of a new drug
called "Astra-dopa," a type of long-acting levodopa.

The first day or so at the Center I felt as if I had
found a protective haven and new hope for the future.
But during the next few days my feelings of security
and hope gave way to fear and distrust.

This was my sixth admission as an inpatient. The
hospital wing had become much more crowded and
the staff much busier than three years earlier, when I
had been spoiled by an eager staff that temporarily
outnumbered the patients. Now I had to wait until the

doctor came on rounds to talk to him and even then he was able to give me very little time.

During my first stay, the treatment had been so successful the entire staff shared my enthusiasm. Now, some seemed to share my depression.

"You're scared; that's your trouble," said one hospital aide. He was right. But telling me so didn't help. I was scared further when I talked with a former roommate who had already started on the same drug study I was to begin soon. The doctor had told me that my friend was doing well but the patient gave an entirely different report. He looked and sounded depressed. His description of the shock experienced when his previous medication had been withdrawn reminded me of a recent similar experience, the memory of which still gave me nightmares. About a year earlier my medication had been withdrawn in anticipation of a minor surgical procedure which proved to be unnecessary. But the sixteen-hour period without anti-Parkinson medication caused me to become almost completely immobile.

With that unpleasant memory vividly aroused, I hunted for the doctor in charge of the experimental program to seek an explanation for the difference between his report and that of my former roommate. When I found him he was too busy to talk to me. After I waited for several hours, my agitated state advanced to near panic and I informed one of the assistant physicians that I had changed my mind—I didn't want to participate in the study. I told him of my fears. When I finally did get to talk to the neurologist in charge, he explained that since the mission of NIH is research, I couldn't be kept on as an inpatient without being on a study. He agreed to keep me on as an outpatient until I either found private help or decided I could be a cooperative experimental subject.

Debbie and I decided to seek private help. We took the train to New York to consult a neurologist who was noted both as a clinical researcher and a skillful physician. After a lengthy examination and discussion, he concluded that my condition could be improved by taking me off my medication for awhile and starting all over to build up my dosage of levodopa more slowly than it had been originally. The treatment would require about four weeks of hospitalization. But, he believed that the trauma of staying in a hospital 250 miles from home for a month should be avoided if at all possible.

"Do you know any private neurologists in Washington?" he asked. I named one we had read about who was associated with a medical school and hospital and who had access to the same experimental drugs I was taking at NIH. The consultant said he'd read some of the man's papers and they had impressed him favorably. We took this to be a recommendation and arranged to see the Washington neurologist as soon as possible after we got home.

"I think I can help you without withdrawing your present medication or putting you in the hospital," he said during our first visit. "I plan to continue you on your present regimen of levodopa and MK-486, but I'll gradually switch you over to a substitute for MK-486 which seems to work better. However, if you become my patient, you must agree to follow my instructions strictly. I don't want you making variations in your dosage. Remember, I'm the doctor, you're the patient."

"If you can help me, I'll be glad to follow your instructions," I said. I also agreed to pay a substantial

fee for each visit, even though I was to be an experimental patient.

For the first month or so the instructions of our new
neurologist were so helpful he seemed to prove the old
adage that "you get what you pay for." But within
three months my condition deteriorated so badly I was
forced to retire from work.

First, the new doctor prescribed a sleeping pill. The
same pill had been suggested previously by doctors at
NIH but was resisted by my wife and me because of
our concern over the possibility I might become ad-
dicted to it. When I mentioned this concern to the
new neurologist he said, "You're already so dependent
on drugs, it's silly to worry about a mild sleeping pill
such as Dalmane. And if it enables you to sleep
through the night, you'll gain two ways. You'll get a
respite from the powerful medication you're taking
and you'll get more continuous sleep, which you badly
need." He certainly was correct. I was soon able to
sleep through most nights until 5:00 or 6:00 A.M., thus
eliminating my previous 2:00 A.M. dosage of L-Dopa
and a long and unpleasant interruption to my rest.
This gave me much more energy and less dyskinesia.
When he learned that I was, in effect, eating six meals a
day in order to balance food and medication with each
dose, he prescribed three regular meals with a slightly
larger dosage of L-Dopa at mealtimes to compensate
for the interference of protein and certain other foods.
He reduced the dosage of L-Dopa between meals and
prescribed very small snacks to be taken at these times.

This change had social as well as medical benefits
and enabled me to lead a more normal life. But the
basic treatment provided by my new doctor seemed to
me to be disastrous. The major change was the substi-
tution of Aldomet, a drug normally used to lower

blood pressure, to act as a potentiator of L-Dopa instead of MK-486.[3]

Our new professor-neurologist was one of a few researchers in the country using Aldomet on an experimental basis. He told us it appeared that Aldomet caused less dyskinesia than MK-486 and gave a more even, dependable response.

Aldomet certainly did cut down on my uncontrollable movements and it calmed me down quite a bit— so much so that I was often barely able to move at all; I was very sleepy and groggy most of the time, and it seemed to me that the effects of my medications were becoming increasingly less predictable.

Perhaps the researcher-physician was more objective than I give him credit for, but he appeared to be so eager to prove the superiority of "his" experimental drug that he subconsciously discounted its failures and accentuated its successes. I would come to my visits with a list of complaints and problems and would be told how much better I was doing on Aldomet. I found I was not the only patient experiencing this phenomenon.

"I keep telling him I'm getting worse and he tells me I'm getting better," another patient said to me.

At the time he was adjusting my dosage of Aldomet, I was preparing for some important meetings and activities at work.

"I'm supposed to speak to a convention group in Cleveland next week," I told him. "The way I've been feeling lately, I don't see how I can make the trip. Do you think I should cancel out?" I asked.

He gave me his typical response: "Don't worry. Go about your normal business and you'll be all right."

I did worry, but I did go to the convention. And I

---

[3]Now known as carbidopa.

was far from all right. My first major problem occurred at the Cleveland airport. Walking across the waiting room I froze in my tracks and hung on to a railing of some kind, unable to even speak loudly enough to ask for help. Fortunately a passing "Good Samaritan" noticed my predicament and got an airline agent to bring me a wheelchair. After resting for three-quarters of an hour and taking extra medication, I was able to make it to a cab to go to the convention hall. However, I got only halfway down the hall to the meeting room when the invisible gremlin glued my shoes to the floor again. I sat down right where I was on the dirty hallway floor, fortunately close enough to a wall to use as a back rest. A passing friend recognized me and found a chair for me to sit on. Imagine my discomfort, however, when I noticed that my seat was located right outside the men's room. When the meeting session ended, hordes of people filled the hallway and hundreds brushed past me.

Desperately seeking rest and escape from an embarrassing situation, I closed my eyes. But I couldn't keep them closed long. It seemed that half the people streaming by recognized me and had some curious, friendly, or sympathetic comment to make. "I'll never relax enough to make that meeting," I thought. In desperation I popped an extra dose of L-Dopa. After awhile it worked. But within minutes I was uncontrollably mobile. I staggered into the meeting attempting to be inconspicuous, but I had the feeling that every eye was glued on me, observing my strange movements—head waving back and forth, arms flailing, and body shifting on the chair. When I was asked to tell about the NEA's bicentennial project, "Education for Better International Understanding," and to ask for the cooperation of the group, my voice was so wavery

I could scarcely be understood. The group, however, obviously sympathized with my condition and appreciated my determination to fulfill my mission. They pledged their support and I lined up a valuable consultant for the project.

"See, it worked out well," the doctor said when, upon my return home, I told him of my experiences. He seemed to ignore the freeze-ups. But I couldn't forget.

"A very important meeting is coming up in a few days," I told the doctor. "This time it's at NEA Headquarters, but it involves some very important people, including my immediate boss and the president and vice-president of the NEA. If there's any danger of my freezing up, I'd rather postpone the meeting or stay away."

"Don't worry. Go about your normal business," came the standard advice.

"OK. You're the doctor," I responded blithely, thinking, "All's well that ends well."

But this time things didn't end well at all—at least not for me. I got so stiff during the meeting that I couldn't get my pills out of my pocket. A colleague fed me the pills and held a cup of water to my mouth. I was barely able to swallow. Then came one of the most unpleasant hours of my life. While the committee tried to carry on the discussion, I squirmed and fidgeted, trying desperately to regain control over my body and voice.

But the harder I tried, the tighter my muscles became. When my wife—who had been sent for—arrived to take me home, I had to be lifted into a wheelchair to reach, first the bathroom, and then our automobile.

That was my last day of regular work at the NEA. I

was gently told to get under better control before coming back to work.

Debbie drove me directly to the doctor. He seemed to anticipate what was on my mind.

"For whatever reason," he said, "you don't seem to be satisfied with my care. I can arrange for you to go back to NIH."

"Perhaps that would be best," I said, trying to be casual, but so eager to return to NIH that I felt like jumping up and down.

And so in April 1973, I returned to NIH with a heightened appreciation for the quality of care given to experimental patients there. My absence had also made the NIH heart grow fonder toward me, it seemed.

"We're glad to have you back," the clinical director told me. "Because of the nature of your condition and your ability to observe and record accurately, you're one of our most valuable experimental patients."

"I'll try to stay that way," I replied gratefully. "Now, do you think you can get me into good enough shape to go back to work?" I asked. "I've been given three months on sick leave to improve enough to pass examination by NEA-appointed physicians; otherwise I'll have to go on disability retirement."

"We'll try our best, is all I can say," he said. "But we have no dramatic new treatment to offer you. We can only make some adjustments in your previous regimen."

Adjustments were made, and I showed some improvement, but not enough to enable me to go back to work. When the three months were up, there was mutual agreement that I was unable to continue. On September 1, 1973, I officially began retirement due to disability.

PHASE III

Accommodation
Without Surrender

12 *Adjusting to Retirement*

ACCEPTING RETIREMENT at age forty-eight was as difficult as accepting the diagnosis eleven years earlier that I had parkinsonism. It took Debbie and me quite a while to acknowledge "permanent disability" as really permanent, but eventually we did. And when we did we were able to apply one of our favorite adages: "If you get a lemon, make lemonade."

As we learned to adjust to retirement we found some advantages in my relief from the pressures of time and responsibility. Retirement enabled us to enjoy our lives more, to cope more effectively with my ailment, to improve our relationships with our children, and to render increased service to others.

Like many other couples, Debbie and I had feared that too much togetherness might break our already strained marital relationship. However, within a year after retirement our love and respect for each other began to increase. After more than twenty-five years of frustration over differing attitudes and habits on a few crucial matters we began to accommodate to each other. My adjustment to retirement was aided also by the introduction of a new medication that increased my ability to function—not enough to resume remunerative work—but enough to improve my roles as husband and parent.

Our adjustment began with advance planning before

actual retirement. In this important step, we had the invaluable help of a psychiatric social worker from NIH. During the previous few years, he had already laid the groundwork for our emotional adjustment to retirement. We had expressed concerns about our children. In response he kept emphasizing in different ways that if we wanted our children to be happy and fulfilled, the best thing we could do was to be as happy and fulfilled as possible ourselves. Our children's emotional well-being would automatically benefit from our example.

Financial planning was another important step. With the help of the benefits expert at the NEA and the social worker at NIH, I calculated what my income would be for as far ahead as I could project. The financial prospects seemed surprisingly good because, in addition to a pension from the NEA and Social Security disability payments, I had three insurance policies that paid fairly substantial sums for the first five years of retirement, plus income from savings and investments. When I took into account tax savings and other financial advantages of retirement, I felt quite relaxed about the long-term financial picture.

It took quite a bit of effort, however, to make Debbie feel financially secure. For throughout our married life, differences in our attitude towards money had been a major wedge between us.

When we were first married, I felt lucky that she was frugal because it enabled us to save money even out of my three-thousand-dollar-a-year teacher's salary. As my salary grew to ten times that amount, and we acquired additional capital through gifts and inheritance, the need for penury disappeared, but the habit persisted. Debbie bought very few new clothes for herself or for the children, using hand-me-downs as much as possible.

One day I overheard one of our daughters say to her older brother: "Those are nice pajamas, Art. When they get old and worn and torn, can I have them?" Had I felt more relaxed, I probably would have laughed and taken some action to correct the situation without letting it become a big issue. But the general tension I felt because of my parkinsonism caused me to over-react and to feel so emotionally upset that I couldn't talk about the problem rationally with Debbie. So, one more resentment was left unresolved to fester and spawn further resentment.

When I was on extended sick leave, however, I took the time to show my wife in detail, projected over the next ten years, exactly what our income would be and what our financial needs might be. I used all the techniques of good teaching that I could muster, and they worked. Finally, Debbie began to relax about the future, and started to spend more in the present on things she had long neglected, such as her own ward-robe or trips she had been eager to take.

When I didn't feel up to taking a trip with her, I would urge her to go alone or with someone else. During my retirement, she began to take me up on such offers. Relief from the daily drudgery of dealing with parkinsonism and the stimulation from new ex-periences did her much good. And even did me some good. I enjoyed her experiences vicariously through slides and verbal descriptions, and I benefited from her emotional relief.

One day a week Debbie worked as a volunteer nurse at one of the hospitals where she had formerly helped train surgical technicians. She also lectured on behalf of the American Cancer Society to women's groups on how to detect possible breast cancer. And she worked part-time for pay in the Employee Health Center at NIH. So most days, she was away from home for at least a few hours. These activities tired her physically, but refreshed her emotionally and enabled me to have time alone to rest or poke along at my own rate on my various projects.

Another matter on which we differed as much as Jack Spratt and his wife was neatness around the house. Debbie was a meticulous housekeeper, believing in "a place for everything and everything in its place." I was sloppy. This may seem like a trivial matter, but it is a serious source of friction among many couples. With the added time and energy I had in retirement, therefore, I made a concerted effort to organize my things so that I would not upset the security which Debbie got from orderliness. I soon found that orderliness gave me a feeling of security, too. In return, Debbie learned to tolerate with good grace a little more disorder than she had before.

In our most difficult and most rewarding act of accommodation, we came to closer agreement on our philosophies of child rearing and education.

Debbie had been brought up in a very authoritarian atmosphere, both in New England schools and in her home. I, on the other hand, had been trained, especially in teacher education, and somewhat in my home background, to be more permissive. My objective was to help children find their own way.

The luxury of time for discussion during retirement enabled us to agree that neither one of us alone had the right answer. We concluded that the best way to raise children was through a combination of firm guidance *and* respect for self-development. Practicing this philosophy improved our relationship with our children, even those who had already left the nest.

The seemingly trivial details of daily living also required readjustment during retirement.

When I was employed, the routines required by work shaped and developed my habits of living. What time I got up, when I ate my meals, when I went to the bathroom, when I could relax, were all more or less determined for me. But upon retirement, I nearly drowned in an ocean of decisions to be made. Every act required rescheduling and readjusting. At times I was almost paralyzed by the choices.

I felt like the centipede who had managed to walk quite well until he was asked: "How do you coordinate those numerous legs of yours? How do you know which leg to move first?" When the centipede tried to figure out how, he got so confused he stumbled all over himself. For walking, habit had served him better than considered action.

Similarly, humans need to carry out the routines of life fairly automatically if they are to have the time and energy for creative living. I tried to work out a regular schedule so that many routines of living could become automatic. For example, I would arise about the same time each day, even though there was no pressure to do so. Regularity enabled me to keep the same medication schedule each day so that taking my pills could be semi-automatic.

I found that it was helpful to structure my day around some purposeful activity. Writing about my experiences with parkinsonism and as an experimental patient served as my "anchor" activity. I determined which few hours a day I felt best able to write and built a schedule around those hours.

I tried to arise, eat, move my bowels, exercise, and

go to bed at regular times. I also tried to stick to my schedule for taking medication more rigidly than in the past. Instead of taking emergency doses of medication when I felt unable to move, I took emergency rests.

Thus, I was able to reduce some of the adverse effects I had suffered from too much medication. I still experienced wide fluctuations in my condition. But gaining more control over my life in retirement enabled me to anticipate somewhat when my better times would be and to make maximum use of such times for work, play, or socialization, and to rest or do something easy and private during my worst times. Of course I could not always predict my condition and was grateful for the patience of my family and friends in coping with my sudden spells of inability to walk or talk.

These spells were part of the "on-off" effect which some patients who had been taking L-Dopa for several years were experiencing. Doctors use this term to refer to rapid transitions from excessive looseness (dyskinesia) to stiffness or vice versa.

I remember how this "on-off" effect affected me when my wife and I and another couple had dined at a fashionable restaurant in a hotel near our home. During dinner I was so dyskinetic I tipped over my water glass and scattered food off my plate in all directions. When we finished dinner, I felt no difficulty in walking until we reached the lobby. Suddenly as I got close to a crowd, I froze in my tracks. I could not take a single step more, and had I not been supported by my wife and friend, I would have slipped to the floor. They practically carried me to a nearby couch and stretched me out on it. I had to rest there for over an hour before I could move.

One of the most helpful things my wife did during the years I was having the "on-off" effect was to maintain as regular a social life for both of us as possible. We went to and gave dinner parties, attended the theater, and took walks with friends, never certain that I wouldn't suddenly become stiff and have to sit or lie down wherever I was.

I recall several other occasions when I lay stretched out on the couch of a hotel lobby, the grass adjoining a hiking trail, or the rug in a corner of a theater lobby, with Debbie standing or sitting nearby, pretending to be unaware of the curious stares of passersby. For those who wanted to help or further satisfy their curiosity, she had simple, matter-of-fact responses. "He'll be all right in a little while. He just needs to rest," or "No, he doesn't need an ambulance. It's a neurological disorder that isn't dangerous. His medication needs time to work."

I was so embarrassed I often closed my eyes, pretending I wasn't there. But as long as Debbie and our friends were willing to drive me and to endure awkward situations, I decided to risk the discomfort we often experienced rather than withdraw into a private shell.

My adjustment to retirement was further aided by the continued friendship of former work colleagues. They helped me feel that I was still part of the organization. I also found emotional support through active participation in the NEA Retired Employees Association.

After I retired, the NEA gave an enduring boost to my ego. My last achievement for the Association had been to focus attention on celebrating the U.S. bicentennial observance by teaching for peace. The NEA Bicentennial Committee established an annual award to the state and national teacher organizations that made the "most significant contributions in the implementation of the 'world community' concept." The award was named the "Dorros Peace Award."

As I found some success in coping with my illness and received comments from other parkinsonians, indicating that they had been encouraged and helped by information and attitudes I had conveyed to them, I gave more attention to writing about parkinsonism and less to the proposed book about raising one's children in the suburbs. Soon I suspended the latter project altogether.

Despite my improved morale and some temporary improvement in my ability to do things, the debilitating effects of the ailment and the toxic effects of continued large doses of powerful medication gradually took their toll. Increasingly, I felt groggy and as if there was a haze between me and the rest of the world. I could concentrate for only about an hour at a time when I was in good condition, and I could write or typewrite only a few hundred words before getting stiff and tremulous.

I tried dictating into a cassette recorder from which my wife or a friend transcribed. But this had its problems, too, as my enunciation was often unclear or I lost track of what I had said and repeated or missed information. But although my rate of output was only a fraction of that of a normal writer, I continued to plod along, scrawling with a pen, pecking at the typewriter keys, or mumbling into a microphone.

Just as I was bogging down almost completely, a chance meeting with an old friend recharged me. The friend, who hadn't seen me for several years, owned an electronic manufacturing firm. As we got reacquainted, he became interested in my writing and my problems in using a tape recorder. "I'll get you some equipment that will be sensitive enough to pick up your voice even when it's weak and won't develop a lot of interfering sound when you move around," he promised.

Sure enough, in a few days he presented me with a small portable recorder and clip-on extension microphone that got good reproduction both when I was stiff and when I was dyskinetic. I'm not sure which inspired me more—the act of friendship or the improved recordings—but I spurted ahead again on this book.

I was further inspired to write about parkinsonism from the patient's point of view when I discovered Dr. Oliver Sacks's book *Awakenings* shortly after it was published in 1974. His clear and dramatic statements about how to cope with parkinsonism crystallized my own experiences and observations into a working philosophy which has proven vital to my well-being. To a certain extent, my autobiographical account is a case study of a patient who tries to apply Sacks's "accommodation" approach.

Debbie, too, found comfort and help in Sacks's book; but even so, the strain of having to cope with me full time was wearing down her spirit and physical stamina. In tape-recorded recollections of that period she said: "We both get depressed. But, fortunately, most of the time we don't both get depressed at the same time so we're able to help each other out of it."

We were aided, also, in our struggle against depression by the hope that another medical breakthrough would come in time to be of help. And it did. It was a new medication named bromocriptine.

13 Bromocriptine to the Rescue

AS DEBBIE and I waited our turn to see a doctor one Thursday in January, 1975, the halls of the NIH Parkinson Outpatient Clinic were buzzing with rumors about a new "miracle" drug.

"The new English doctor had success with it in London. That's why he was brought to NIH, to introduce it to the United States," we were told by a friend as we waited to see the neurologist.

When Debbie and I went in to confer with the doctor, we learned that the rumors were partly true. It is not true that bromocriptine is a "miracle drug" in the sense that it provides a cure or even complete alleviation of symptoms, the doctor told us. It *is* true that in the London experiment, bromocriptine had provided some reduction of Parkinson symptoms, especially in more advanced cases of the ailment and for patients who had been taking L-Dopa or Sinemet for several years.[1] Some of the patients obtained a reduction of dyskinesia and the "on-off" effect. However, the new drug produced some of the same adverse side effects as L-Dopa.

What we were happiest to learn was that the drug would be offered to carefully selected experimental patients at NIH.

---

[1] The brand name under which bromocriptine is available in the U.S. is Parlodel.

"You seem to be a good candidate for the bromocriptine study because you have a severe 'on-off' effect which may be relieved. And your health is such that you're likely to be able to tolerate the new medication."

We were told that the known side effects, should they occur, were not life threatening and could be reversed by dropping the medication. The relative safety of the drug had been tested not only by animals and Parkinson patients but by a much larger number of people who were given the drug for much different purposes. It had been used in Europe for several years, especially for "suppression of lactation" or, in lay language, "for drying up mother's milk."

"How is drying up mother's milk related to parkinsonism?" I asked. "How did it ever occur to you to even try it for such a different purpose? Or was its effectiveness for parkinsonism discovered accidently by some tremulous women with unwanted lactation?"

Our physician answered that the decision to try bromocriptine for parkinsonism indicates how far research has progressed in the last ten years or so. New knowledge about pharmacology and how the brain and nerves work has enabled researchers to deliberately pick bromocriptine as a possible aid to Parkinson patients. They knew from animal studies with bromocriptine that it is a dopamine agonist. That is, it helps activate pathways in the nervous system just as dopamine does. But dopamine cannot be given directly to patients. It must be manufactured by the body from levodopa. Thus levodopa works indirectly while bromocriptine acts directly. So even if bromocriptine turns out to be disappointing itself, it may be the precursor of other more effective medications that work in a new and more efficient way.

"That's why we plan a comprehensive, double-blind study at NIH lasting at least six months and perhaps several years. What we learn about bromocriptine may help us find improved treatments for parkinsonism and other neurological ailments," he said.

The researcher then explained that I could participate in the experiment as an outpatient. At first, I would have to come to the clinic weekly, then less frequently. On each visit I would be examined by two neurologists. The first would decide when and how much bromocriptine to give me. The pills would be coded, though, so that I would be "blind" to what I was taking. The second examining neurologist would also be "blind" to the content of the red capsules. He would assess my Parkinson condition as objectively as possible, rating me on factors such as tremors, rigidity, gait, balance, posture, finger dexterity, facial expression, rising from a chair, and speech. A psychologist would also check me on each visit. Blood and urine samples would be collected and analyzed frequently for my protection and also for more information about the effects of the drug. Near the end of the experiment, records of the "blind" observers would be compared to the coded record of my prescribed medications to be used in assessing the effectiveness of the drug.

We were told that a double-blind study of a new drug is usually the standard way to be sure that it is the drug itself and not the patient's or doctor's expectations that is helping the patient; for it has been demonstrated many times that some patients, when told they are receiving a drug that will alleviate symptoms of an ailment, find relief even if the pill contains no medication at all. This is called the "placebo effect." Thus, to keep patient and doctor as objective as possible in a double-blind experiment, the patient and at least one observer are "blind" to how much medication the patient is getting. All the capsules look alike but may be of varying strength or may have no medication in them at all (placebos).

I started taking the "mystery pills," code numbered but not named, in February. Within a month I began to feel different and so assumed (correctly) that I was getting the bromocriptine rather than the placebo. At first there was no obvious difference in my appearance or movement; I just felt better internally—more confident, optimistic, and energetic. After a few months my condition improved so much that the "blind" neurologist observer could not contain his excitement about my condition. He exclaimed to my wife, "I haven't been told whether he's taking a placebo or bromocriptine, but he's walking better, his balance is better, he has practically no stiffness, his expression is almost normal, his speech is stronger—he must be on bromocriptine."

In relating this incident to me later, my wife said, "He wasn't telling me anything I didn't know but it's good to see that researchers are human too."

By July I felt so much better that my wife and I planned a two-week vacation trip centered around a visit to our older son in Seattle, Washington. The neurologist managing my medication said he still couldn't tell me what and how much medication I was taking but that in order to facilitate our vacation he would keep the dosage the same during the vacation as it had been the previous week.

As I learned when the experiment was over, I had not yet reached my optimum dose at that time. This caused some dramatic difficulties during the trip; but we were able to adjust to these difficulties and not let them spoil what turned out to be one of the most exciting and enjoyable trips we ever had together. We viewed the slides taken on that trip so many times we almost bleached the color out of them—reliving our memories of the house that our son rebuilt, and our hike across the snow fields at Mount Rainier, our cruises on Puget Sound, visits to beautiful Victoria, Canada, and Buchart Gardens, our climb on the giant driftwood on the beach at La Push, our view of the masses of wild flowers on Hurricane Ridge, our walks through the Rain Forest, our shopping and eating trips to Pike Street Market, and much more.

We saw and did more than many healthier travelers. How did we manage? Through very careful planning. This included dividing the trip into several side trips of a few days each with a return for rest and recuperation to our home base, our son's house, between trips. To follow our own interests or because I needed to rest, we also did some things separately several times.

Another helpful strategy was to explain my condition simply and matter-of-factly during our initial contacts with motel managers, tour guides, and others whose concern or curiosity might otherwise be aroused. For example, as we joined a group of tourists assembling outside the lodge at Mt. Rainier for a guided hike to view a glacier, I told the ranger-leader in a voice loud enough for the others to hear, "Don't be concerned if you see me having difficulty walking. I take medication for a neurological condition that works very erratically. Sometimes I move too freely and sometimes I get very stiff. So my wife and I will just stay at the edge of the group and if we fall behind don't worry. We'll either catch up or wait for your return, but we won't wander off."

"Do you have Parkinson's disease?" the ranger

asked. "My father has it and I know what to expect. I'm glad you mentioned it because there are two routes I could take and I can use you as an excuse to take the longer but easier route."

Not all our contacts were so considerate. For example, there was the bus driver who would not let me board his bus which was only a few feet away from where I was waiting. He had many empty seats in the bus but he insisted that I had to get on the "second section" which was at a distant part of the terminal because his bus gave priority to ferry passengers. At the time I was unable to walk, but no amount of explaining or pleading changed his mind, and Debbie, with some help from bystanders, finally dragged me and our luggage to the distant bus. The second driver helped me on the bus, tried to put me at ease and apologized for the action of the other driver. "He could have taken you on," he said, "but he's got a mean streak in him."

So even the best made plans sometimes go awry and call for another quality in parkinsonians and their families—the tolerance of considerable embarrassment. On that trip I made such great progress in sacrificing my pride to reality that I allowed my wife to borrow a wheelchair for me to get to the plane on our return flight. This made boarding so much easier for both of us than debarking had been when we had landed in Seattle. On that occasion I'd said I didn't need a wheelchair, then I froze in the middle of the airport and had to be carried to a seat to wait half an hour for my medication to work.

After our return, I had to pay part of the price of being an experimental patient—I had to undergo the placebo phase of the experiment. Of course, I was not told that I was being taken off bromocriptine, but this soon became evident and I had an uncomfortable few weeks. During that time, I didn't know what to expect. As my dosage of bromocriptine was slowly cut back and the levodopa increased, my body had to readjust to dependence on levodopa without bromocriptine. There was a marked regression in my condition.

By the end of the summer when I was back on levodopa alone, I felt miserable physically, but very healthy psychologically—because I knew that eventually my parkinsonism would be relieved somewhat by the combination of bromocriptine and Sinemet which had proven helpful in the first phase of the experiment. The researchers put their notes together to determine what my optimum dosage had been during the first phase of the study and I was slowly restored to that regimen, this time with eyes wide open. The euphoria I experienced as I returned to optimum is recorded in daily notes I made at the time. Here are some excerpts:

Thursday, September 11, 1975, was a turning point! This has been my first really good day since going off bromocriptine in August during the double-blind study. Active all morning. No drop off. No nap after lunch. Felt tired and slightly stiff about three. Rested about twenty minutes and felt fine. Worked in back yard. Was overdosed.

September 12. Was able to swim without getting breathing out of timing.

September 14. Each day seems to get better, including my feelings of confidence and optimism about the future.

Tonight was Yom Kippur Eve, and for the first time in several years I could feel enthusiastic about asking the Lord to inscribe me in the Book of Life for another year.

September 17. Another landmark! When I woke up this morning, I found that there was only one me instead of a left side and a right side—a left side that had to be pretty much dragged along by the right. I could feel very little difference in muscular tension or otherwise on my right and left sides. And after a full calisthenics workout before breakfast, I was able to do a fair amount of jogging in place and feel very comfortable about it instead of the usual jerkiness or tightening of my left calf.

September 18. Another happy day. Today I've been able to function all day even when I felt slightly overdosed or underdosed. I never got frozen or incapacitated entirely. Also, my psychological outlook, my clarity of thinking, my ability to plan ahead and think ahead, my ability to do things of every kind seem to be increasing each day.

October 2. I can tell I'm walking much better now because little children don't run after me laughing or mimicking me.

October 4. Today I'm enjoying the beginning of a weekend at the beach with some friends in a manner which I could not have hoped to do for the past several years. I was able to leave the group and plunged into the foaming ocean waves and emerged from a brief swim flushed with elation. As we sat on the Ocean City Beach contemplating the beauty of the waves, my friends commented on the wonder of my new-found vigor. "The change in you is remarkable," I was told.

"I know someone else who started in the same experimental study you did," another friend commented, "but he dropped out and of those remaining many don't have significant benefits such as you have."

"How come bromocriptine is doing so well by you?" someone asked.

Exhibit 1

July 26, 1976

**Improvements in Condition
After One Year on Bromocriptine**

A self-evaluation by Sidney Dorros and wife with the aid of written and typed notes made through the year.

Before (Sinemet Only) (About 1750 mg daily)	After (Sinemet and Bromocriptine) (100 mg bromo, 625 mg Sinemet daily)
1. Usually felt groggy or as if there was a haze between me and the world. Was often depressed.	1. Usually have feeling of well-being. Mood is usually happier, more positive, optimistic.
2. Had many cycles during day. Went from extremes of akinesia to dyskinesia. Was taking medication every hour and a half, sometimes more often.	2. Take medication very regularly. Sinemet every 2½ hrs. Bromo only every 5 hrs. Immobility much rarer, although dyskinesia is still serious problem.
3. Hardly able to do anything requiring muscular strength or coordination.	3. Able to do much more. Occasionally mowing lawn, raking, gardening, even some digging and carrying, working on engines, rewiring stove, touch-typing.
4. Couldn't concentrate for long. Disorganized. Difficult to	4. Able to concentrate for longer periods of time. More

"Maybe because I'm trying to do well by it," I replied. "I don't just sit back and dare it to work. I try to help it along. Being retired helps, too, since I'm under less pressure than those who have to work for a living. Also, I've learned to accept a reasonable

Before (Sinemet Only) (About 1750 mg daily)	After (Sinemet and Bromocriptine) (100 mg bromo, 625 mg Sinemet daily)
focus on other people's concerns.	lucid. Able to write (compose) better. Able to consult with wife and children more on their concerns.
5. Ate very carefully because so many foods seemed to interfere with action of Sinemet. Was steadily losing weight.	5. Not nearly as responsive to food intake. Able to eat much more without getting stiff. Gained a few pounds in last month.
6. Was frequently sleepy during the day.	6. Sleepy less often.
7. Afraid to take trips or enter crowded places because of a number of bad experiences in freezing up.	7. Increasing confidence and ability to go out among people and to travel.
8. Frequent urination (about every hour and a half) and dribbling afterward.	8. Urinate much less often (about every 3-4 hours) and rarely dribble afterward.
9. Great difficulty sleeping. Took sleeping pill and still felt compelled to get up in middle of night.	9. Dropped sleeping pill about six weeks ago. Sleep longer. Sometimes to 5:00 or 6:00 A.M.
10. Looked drawn and tired.	10. Many people have told me I look much better.
11. Distinct difference in feeling between left and right sides of body.	11. More even feeling when I'm well-balanced. Still big difference when I'm over or underdosed.

amount of discomfort caused by side effects of powerful medications. For example, there was a stage when I had cramps in my legs, but by adjustment of exercise, rest, diet, and dosage and sheer passage of time, I eventually got rid of the cramps. And because I've learned not to expect a cure or complete alleviation of symptoms, I'm happier than some of the other patients with small improvements and that happiness makes the small improvements bigger. Also, somehow I *expected* bromocriptine to work and it met my expectations."

Nevertheless, during the next year or so, I continued to have erratic responses to my medications and constantly sought to readjust the dosage, my eating habits, and other factors in the elusive search for perfect balance. Yet, overall, the combination of bromocriptine and Sinemet seemed distinctly better than Sinemet alone. (See Exhibit 1.)

The improvement, however, was accompanied by a number of problems, as I noted a year later:

After One Year on Bromocriptine

Impatient
I am often edgy, nervous, impatient.

Frequent Dyskinesia
According to my wife, my dyskinesia is not as severe as it was before; but it seems worse to me. Perhaps it seems so because my tolerance has been worn down or my patience worn thin. At any rate it often prevents me from walking or doing anything requiring coordination.

Digestive and Elimination Problems
Although there seems to have been great improvement in recent months I still have a great deal of flatulence and gas pains. I need to urinate during the night. I usually have some discomfort

in the groin and abdomen areas at night interfering with my sleep.
I eliminate what seems to me an abnormally large amount of
feces. Apparently, I don't fully digest my food.

Inadequate Rest

I still don't feel adequately rested. In addition to the problems
listed above that disturb my sleep at night, I find that if I try to
rest during the day for more than fifteen minutes I have severe
dyskinesia when I get up. At night, although I fall asleep promptly, I often half wake up feeling over-stimulated. It seems that I can
rest only so long as I'm utterly exhausted.

Frustration

My general feeling of well-being often makes me feel as if I can
do more than my body will carry out. The above problems, plus
occasional stiffness and slowness of movement, interfere often
enough so that I don't feel able to definitely count on accomplish-
ing a given task, especially if time pressure is involved. However,
the occasional times when I feel "almost normal" cause me to
hope that if only a little better adjustment of medication and
regimen could be achieved I could function much better.

I am still seeking that "little better adjustment" of
medication and regimen, but I have found that better
adjustment is achieved also by getting out of one's
shell of self-concern and helping others.

14 And He Taketh Away

FOR OVER A DOZEN YEARS I had been receiving a great amount of physical and emotional support from Debbie. By 1976, I had become very dependent on her to run our household, solve family problems, maintain social relationships, transport me around, and cope with the many problems of my illness.

Then a sudden collapse of Debbie's health and strength reversed our roles within a few weeks: She became the patient and I the nurse. The small improvement in my mobility induced by bromocriptine coupled with a strong motivation to help Debbie enabled me to return a little of the aid and comfort she had given me for so long.

First she developed severe back pain which confined her to bed for two weeks. But shortly after she resumed normal activities, a much greater tragedy struck—the belated discovery of breast cancer. This seemed especially terrible because Debbie had lectured on early detection of cancer for the American Cancer Society.

When she discovered a small lump in her breast, she went to see a surgeon whom she knew well and whose competence she respected.

He checked the small growth, said he thought it was not malignant, and suggested that she come back in six months for another examination. Six months later, however, she took a complete physical in an experimental, computerized medical program. The physical included a mammogram, a screening method for detecting malignant tumors in the breast—a procedure later discredited. Because the test showed no malignancy, Debbie was lulled into a false sense of security, and she did not go back to her surgeon at the six-month interval he suggested. She waited another six months, and by that time the growth had increased in size.

The doctor again assured her that he felt quite certain it was not malignant. But this time, he did recommend a biopsy. She knew that his practice was to have the biopsy checked while the patient was still on the operating table, and if the growth turned out to be malignant, he would perform breast surgery (a mastectomy) immediately. Neither of us was terribly frightened by this possibility because the doctor had said he was ninety-five percent sure it was benign.

Imagine my concern, therefore, when the operation went on for four and a half hours, without a word coming from the operating room. By that time I suspected the worst. Had a good friend not been with me, I think I would have panicked and broken down completely. When the surgeon called me in to a private room to tell me that the growth was malignant after all and that he had performed a modified radical mastectomy, I felt as though my world had suddenly collapsed. But his manner was so confident, and Debbie and I had so much faith in him that after a few minutes he convinced me that he had gotten all of the malignancy. There was very little chance it had spread to the rest of the body, he said, and if there was any spread, a precautionary dose of chemotherapy would take care of any such problems.

Shortly after Debbie came out of the recovery room, still only semiconscious, her consideration for others came through when I asked her if our daughter Carol could come in and see her. She said, "No, I don't think it would be good for her to see me like this." So Carol waited until Debbie was settled in her room and felt more "presentable."

It took a few days before I realized that even though Debbie was a nurse, she was unprepared for what had happened to her. She did not even know the proper way to keep her arm elevated or what exercises to do to keep her lymph glands from becoming swelled after surgery. Some of her nurses and attendants didn't seem to know what to do after breast surgery either. And the doctor was not around enough to instruct Debbie properly.

She asked for the volunteers she knew were available through a program called "Reach for Recovery" sponsored by the American Cancer Society. These women, who had experienced breast surgery themselves, would come talk to patients, bringing them a kit of items including exercise aids and much useful information. Unfortunately, the doctor's permission was needed before the volunteers could be dispatched. By the time it had been obtained and the request relayed, a week went by—the very time when the information, encouragement, and emotional support were most needed.

When we went to see the surgeon for the first visit after surgery, we asked him whether we shouldn't consult an oncologist (cancer specialist) to administer the chemotherapy. He assured us this was not necessary, that he knew more about it than any oncologist in Washington, especially since his own wife had had a mastectomy five years ago and was still in perfect health. Again, we felt reassured.

Although Debbie had considerable pain and her energy level remained low, she soon tried to resume normal activity. In fact, in addition to her other activities, she began exploring possible ways to improve nursing care for mastectomy patients in Washington hospitals.

She also encouraged me to use my new-found energies from bromocriptine to be as active as possible. I therefore resumed work on this book and spent a good bit of time doing research at the National Medical Library. There I came across a booklet on Parkinson's disease published by the British government in which the following sentence caught my eye: "The sharing of mutual experiences through membership in an organization such as the Parkinson's Disease Society may also help both those affected by parkinsonism and others to find solutions to many of their problems and to break down their sense of social isolation."[1] The booklet gave the name and address of the Parkinson's Disease Society of the United Kingdom to which I wrote for further information. The Society sent me a letter and a sample newsletter and information about organizing local chapters. I had an intuitive feeling that here was my new mission in life, but I submerged this feeling for several months while I gave my attention to easing Debbie's load and to writing this book.

Some of my time and energy also went to editing the newsletter of the NEA Retirees organization and serving as its vice-president.

Soon, however, I felt that nothing was as important

---

[1] Office of Health Economics, *Parkinson's Disease* (London: Office of Health Economics, 1974), p. 22.

as helping Debbie get better medical treatment. Despite continued reassurances from the surgeon who had performed the mastectomy, during the winter and early spring of 1977, she continued to feel tired and to have pain and other symptoms that worried us greatly.

We decided, reluctantly, that we should consult a cancer specialist. But despite Debbie's experience as a nurse, she didn't know an oncologist she thought competent. The specialist our family doctor suggested had frightened Debbie so badly on our first visit she didn't want to go back to him. I called everyone I could think of for alternate suggestions and finally obtained an appointment with a recently trained oncologist who seemed familiar with the latest types of treatment.

I vividly remember the morning we went to see him. He had just returned from a vacation; his office was packed and his phone was backed up with calls. However, as soon as he got a good look at Debbie, who was his first patient, I heard him instruct his nurse to hold all calls while he examined her. Immediately thereafter he had her checked into the emergency room of the George Washington University Hospital. There he had several tests done while she waited for a room to become available. For ten days she stayed in the hospital undergoing a thorough diagnosis and a regimen of chemotherapy. Although she must have experienced great pain during this period, she continued to show a smiling countenance to the world. To friends who visited her, former students who flocked to her bedside when they heard she was in the hospital, and her former colleagues, she gave words of encouragement. She assured our children that she was going to be all right, and she kept telling me that I didn't need to hang around and worry about her; she was getting along fine.

But I did worry about her and I spent much time in the hospital trying to see that she got the best possible care. I remembered that had she not hovered over me when I had brain surgery I probably would not have recovered as well as I did. When I tried to protect her, though, from what I considered unnecessary disturbance by five different interns or doctors taking five identical medical histories she told me, "It's okay. This is a teaching hospital and this is the way they learn." So she cheerfully repeated the same information over and over again even though talking hurt her.

She was discharged from the hospital on June 3 and insisted on keeping our previous arrangements to go to Ocean City. Because she loved the sun, we had rented a condominium on the beach; and she was eager to see the house that our younger son, David, and his friend were building by themselves during their college vacation. Our daughter Carol, fresh from her high-school graduation, joined us, bringing a friend with her.

During our two weeks in Ocean City it was all Debbie could do to struggle down to the beach and sit in the sun. She could hardly walk. And although she let Carol and the rest of us to do more cooking and cleaning than normally, she wouldn't let on that she was having any serious difficulty. On the last night she insisted on joining the group on the boardwalk and walking over a mile and a half.

Back home in Bethesda, she began to fail rapidly.

Ellen, our older daughter, visited for about a week before going to Europe with her husband on a business trip. She was excited about the opportunity to go overseas with her husband, but when she saw her mother's condition she wanted to stay with her. Debbie insisted, however, that Ellen carry out her original plans.

During the week or so that Ellen stayed with us, she and her mother had the best relationship they'd had for many years. Debbie made it clear to Ellen that she was very pleased how she had matured into a responsible adult with a happy marriage. Ellen was extremely helpful; she shopped for her mother, made her more comfortable around the house, and did everything she could to show her love and care.

Debbie must have had some premonition of death during this period. One morning when we were alone, she expressed certain last wishes that have played an extremely important role in my life and the lives of the children.

She spoke especially of her desire that we continue to live as full lives as possible. She expressed her satisfaction with the way all four children had developed and said that we had worried unnecessarily about some of the problems we had along the way. She thanked me for my love and patience and made me feel as if I had done all that I could for her. She said that if she died, she wanted me to remarry without feeling guilty.

She also urged me to continue my activities in helping to organize a parkinsonian self-help group. She made me promise that no matter what happened I would go ahead with the organizing picnic scheduled for August at our house and yard.

That was the only time she ever discussed with me the possibility of death. During the remaining days of her illness she acted as though she expected to come out of her battle winning.

She showed little signs of winning, however. Her

fatigue and pain increased in the next few days. On July 6, 1977, the oncologist hospitalized her for further tests and treatment. The tests showed that the cancer had spread rapidly to various parts of her body.

The next few days were like a nightmare. Debbie got little rest because she was continually being wheeled from one lab to another for multitudes of tests and a few treatments. I stood by most of the day and a good part of the night, largely alone. I was alone partly because Debbie and I didn't want others to know how bad her condition was. We still had hope that she would have a remission and wanted our family to have hope too.

Also, we sought to avoid disrupting what we felt were important enterprises in which our children were engaged. Our older son, Arthur, was completing refinishing a run-down house in Seattle. Ellen was on her first trip to Europe with her husband. Our younger son, David, was engaged building a house. And our younger daughter, Carol, had just started on a summer job with the National Institute of Education in which we were eager for her to succeed.

Somehow I found the strength to function well enough to keep an eye on the care Debbie was getting, to help maintain her morale, and to keep our out-of-town family informed. Our friends were eager to help and offered to stay with me in the hospital.

Debbie was incredibly foresighted and considerate of her survivors. Her uncomplaining, dignified manner and her concern for our welfare made the last days of her life less painful to watch than they would otherwise have been.

Three of our four children were at her bedside a few hours before she died. Even that close to her exit from this world (about 1:00 A.M., July 12, 1977), she kept a cheerful exterior. She asked questions of each child and made encouraging comments. I was the last to see her. Just before the medical staff attached her to mechanical life sustaining machines she said, "We raised four wonderful children, after all, didn't we? Take care of each other."

15 To Life

A SHIVER went down my spine when I first heard a brother-in-law, with drink in hand, say "L'chayim," the conventional Jewish toast. For L'chayim means "to life," and at first it seemed inappropriate while we were in mourning. But the more I thought about it the more appropriate it seemed. I had promised Debbie I would try to live life to the fullest, and her sisters and brother helped me keep this promise.

Instead of crying or asking "Why her?" Debbie's family recalled the enjoyable memories of her life. They remembered that Debbie had received the Guggenheim Award for "Best Bedside Nursing" when she graduated from nurses' training.

"We want to set up a fund in Debbie's memory for a similar purpose—to improve nursing practice," her brother later told me. "It could be a scholarship fund or some other project that you think Debbie was especially interested in."

We honored Debbie's memory by turning quickly to positive action. A fund was established to support in-service education of nurses at the hospital where she was last treated. At this writing there have been three workshops to train nurses in the Dorothy Bretholtz Dorros Care Program and a kit of materials for patients has been prepared.

When my parkinsonism incapacitates me and I can

do nothing but think or search my memories, I am often comforted by the thought that this project has improved the nursing care of hundreds of women already, and will help many more in the future.

Three other major activities that sought to help others kept me busy in a positive way following my wife's death. These were: communicating with my children, working on this book, and helping organize a self-help group for parkinsonians and their families.

Even though my children were all adults, they still seemed to require fatherly and motherly guidance, or at least family leadership. I tried to carry out their mother's role as well as my own. Our common loss brought us all closer together. And I believe that my efforts to help rather than be helped enhanced my children's respect for me and increased their desire to help me. We spoke more frequently, more frankly, and about more substantive issues than ever before, and I learned and gained emotional support from them.

Working on this book was most valuable in giving me a purpose for living. To be more accurate, I should say *thinking* about working on this book because my third activity soon became the most consuming.

I mentioned earlier my accidental discovery of the British Parkinsonian Society, in which local chapters afford members an opportunity to gain moral support from each other and to learn how to cope more effectively with their illness. I found that in this country local organizations existed to bring together the victims of many afflictions such as alcoholism, diabetes, mental illness, and cancer, and that such groups were generally very successful in enhancing and supplementing medical treatment. But I could find no such organization for parkinsonians. Four national organizations raised funds for research and dissemination of information about parkinsonism and its treatment, but none seemed interested at the time in helping organize local self-help groups. This didn't cause me to give up the idea, but merely to put off planting the seed until the ground became more fertile. It didn't take long for that to happen. Self-care and self-help for the chronically ill seem to be ideas whose time has come. And when the time is right for a new social innovation there seems to be widespread "spontaneous conception."

The Parkinsonian Society of Greater Washington (PSGW) is an example of this phenomenon. It was conceived simultaneously by at least half a dozen people who had participated in a discussion group for parkinsonians and their spouses led by an NIH social worker. The social worker stimulated an exchange of experiences by asking questions such as the following: "How did you first accept the fact that you had Parkinson's disease?" "How did your life change?" "How did your children react?" "What happened on your job?" "What happened to relationships between spouses?" "How do you manage to keep busy and cheerful?" "How do you keep purpose in your life?"

She gradually went from simple questions to the deeper and more troublesome ones, such as how to avoid depression. When we got to the more personal, sensitive questions, a number of patients and spouses dropped out of the group, unwilling or unable to face opening difficult emotional territory to the view of others. But there were a core of participants who regularly covered most of the significant problems.

Shortly after Debbie's surgery, the social worker got the idea of preparing a videotape of a composite, simulated discussion, covering some of the major issues of coping with the problems of parkinsonism, as a means of training nurses and other health personnel. The task was both burdensome and exciting. It took so much time I would have dropped out had it not been for Debbie's insistence that I continue. She thought it was doing me good, and she thought that as the patient with the longest experience at NIH with L-Dopa and other experimental drugs, I might have something special to contribute.

To celebrate the final videotaping of the program the social worker and her husband hosted the discussion group at a luncheon in their home. It was there that falling on my face helped crystallize the idea of providing an opportunity for more social activities such as that luncheon.

I had loaded my plate with food from the buffet table and started for a chair in the living room. Unaware that there was a small step down, I stumbled and fell. My plate went flying, scattering food over a ten-foot area. I ended sprawled on my stomach and face, but unhurt. Several people rushed to my rescue and started cleaning up the mess without the excitement there might have been in a "normal" group, since several of the parkinsonians in attendance were accustomed to falling. When they saw I was unhurt, however, a group gathered around to question me on my technique for avoiding injury. After I described and demonstrated my "falling style," others exchanged accounts, serious and humorous, about falling and how to avoid it. At another type of gathering my fall would merely have been embarrassing. But at this meeting of peers it provided a vehicle for learning how to cope with a common problem and also entertainment of a sort.

It was then, in May of 1977, that PSGW was

spontaneously conceived. Several people expressed the desire to get together again for social purposes and to discuss common concerns. I offered the use of my backyard for a pot-luck picnic. We agreed to form a permanent organization if there was enough interest expressed at the picnic.

The picnic was scheduled for the last Saturday in August, which turned out to be a little more than a month after Debbie's death. Several members of the informal organization committee asked if I wanted to change the location of the picnic, but I explained to them that, before she entered the hospital, Debbie had urged me to go ahead "no matter what happens."

At the picnic, reminders of Debbie and of my great loss caused me to take frequent secret crying breaks in the bathroom or upstairs; but I tried in public to reflect the very happy and enthusiastic spirit that prevailed among the adults and the children who attended.

Almost everyone present was in favor of forming a local organization for the purpose of fostering friendships and mutual support among Parkinson patients and families. Two lawyer members and a former Air Force officer volunteered to draw up by-laws, and I was elected acting president.

A second picnic, held in October 1977 in the National Park at Great Falls, Virginia, is memorable for the enthusiasm of the participants who persisted in completing a specially conducted walking tour with a National Park Ranger even though it was raining.

The Parkinsonian Society of Greater Washington was officially launched at a charter meeting in January 1978. At that time we had our first medical informational program. The clinical director for neurological research at NIH who spoke on the topic "Outlook for

Improved Medication" seemed to endorse the Society's approach when he said: "The routine clinical management of the condition, all the details of dealing with routine therapy, with routine everyday issues apart from therapy—these are the main problems of the patients with Parkinson's disease and their physicians."

During the panel discussion following the neurologist's talk, the main purpose of our society was succinctly expressed by one of the founders, George Foster, who said, "We aim to put a smile on the face of every member."

Our objectives as stated in our by-laws were even more ambitious:

> The objectives of this nonprofit organization are to foster the maximum potential for living of Parkinsonians and their families and to aid them in participating in and enjoying the active world. It shall encourage optimism and hope, and counteract despair and depression by providing opportunities for self-help, social contacts, and sharing personal experiences and information about coping with parkinsonism. It shall also seek to help the public and medical personnel understand Parkinsonians as people.

Our membership was broad. It included patients, family members and friends, medical and support personnel.

From the beginning, our program has been diverse. We have always had more imagination and enthusiasm than efficiency. With no paid staff, we are entirely a volunteer organization. But we have the magic ingredient that is more important than efficiency to the success of an organization—we *care*. We care about each other, about ourselves, and about our objectives.

Membership in the Society and the formation of similar groups around the country were stimulated by

a commendation placed in the *Congressional Record* of
January 26, 1978, by Congressman Charles J. Carney,
of Ohio. Mr. Carney, an honorary member of the
Society, had persisted in conducting an active life of
political service even though he had been afflicted with
parkinsonism for thirty years.

His statement in the *Congressional Record*, after urg-
ing greater financial support for medical research, said
that good health cannot be bought entirely and that a
great deal depends on self-help. He had the by-laws of
PSGW published in the *Congressional Record* so that
"they might serve as a model for other communities."

Three years later the Society had about 250 members; an interesting bimonthly newsletter; well attended bimonthly meetings and special social functions in between; weekly exercise programs and discussion groups in each of four different locations; and
a summer camp vacation for parkinsonians and their
families that was so successful it attracted more than
eighty participants in 1980, some coming from states
as far away as Texas.

In an evaluation of our first camp program, I asked:
"What did you enjoy most about the camp?"

The first response was, "The people. The wonderful, accepting, loving people."

In a message to a 1979 symposium to evaluate and
improve our Society, the social worker who helped
launch our group said: ". . . so in thinking over all of
your many accomplishments, I would say at the core
of everything you have done, the most important ones
stand out to be the relationships formed, the reaching
out to those too shy and too reluctant to come forward, the warmth and interest you show for each
other, the helping hand for one more needy, the
encouragement by gentle prodding, and by your shin-

ing example that there is joy to life in spite of difficulties along the way."

No doubt the value of our parkinsonian society is
primarily social and emotional in nature. It does not
attempt to provide or interfere with medical treatment; but through exchange of experiences, speakers,
meetings, and printed sources it disseminates information about parkinsonism and its treatment that busy
doctors often do not have the time to transmit.

Working in a leadership role as president and then
as vice-president of PSGW has provided purpose for
my life. And the example of many of our members
who conduct themselves in a cheerful and dignified
manner, even though they cope with more difficult
problems than I had believed possible, serves as a
continuing inspiration to me to live as full and enjoyable a life as possible.

16 To Love

Because
I have known despair
I value hope

Because
I have tasted frustration
I value fulfillment

Because
I have been lonely
I value love
—Leonard Nimoy

Norman Cousins has publicized the idea that if negative emotions produce negative chemical changes in the body, positive emotions may produce positive chemical changes. Oversimplified reviews of Cousins's account of how he cured himself of an "incurable" illness credit the achievement to humor and massive doses of vitamin C. Actually, Cousins has a much broader approach. He asks, "Is it possible that love, hope, faith, laughter, confidence, and the will to live have therapeutic values?"[1]

---

[1]Norman Cousins, *Anatomy of an Illness as Perceived by the Patient* (New York: W.W. Norton & Co., 1979), p. 35.

I can attest that they have. I believe it's been love and the other positive emotions listed above that have sustained me as much as medicine since the loss of my wife. First, memories of our love and faithfulness to each other for thirty years helped counteract the grief I continued to feel and still feel over her death. Then, just as new medications have appeared to rescue me each time I have come near the bottom physically, new sources of emotional support came forth when my morale needed boosting.

In addition to the increased attention from my children, and other relatives and friends, members of the Parkinsonian Society provided an important source of emotional support. When the leader of a well-financed but differently organized local Parkinson program in another state came to visit PSGW, he observed: "You don't have as much money to work with as we do, but you have a much more important ingredient. You have love!"

But all the emotional supports mentioned above did not keep me from experiencing many hours of loneliness and depression.

When, not long after Debbie's death, I found in my mail invitations from a synagogue-sponsored "singles club," I was depressed even further. "Who would be interested in a middle-aged, chronically ill has been?" I asked myself.

Fortunately, fate provided me with such a person—someone who knew me when I was in my prime and remembered me not as a parkinsonian but, in her words, "as a dynamic and interesting person."

Donna Preudhomme and I had been out of touch ever since she resigned her position as production coordinator of the Publications Division a few years before my retirement. We became reacquainted when

I called her to acknowledge a late condolence note she had sent me. I learned that she was as lonely as I was, for she had been separated from her husband for a few years and recently divorced. She told me, also, that a major reason for her resignation was the belief that I had lost confidence in her abilities.

I explained, belatedly, how my parkinsonism had caused me to be or appear to be impatient, displeased, or threatening. Her reaction: "If I had only known."

"If I had only known" is a reaction which I have heard so often that I wish I had told friends and colleagues more about my illness earlier.

The sound of Donna's voice moved me to invite her to dinner. She accepted and our first date was a great success. We found that we shared many interests in addition to "the good old days" at the NEA. She seemed to be as grateful for my companionship as I was for hers.

We began to see each other frequently and as our friendship advanced to affection and love, I began to feel younger, healthier, and happier. Relatives and friends who spoke with me on the telephone said: "Your voice sounds so much stronger; are you taking a new medication?" "In a way, yes," I was tempted to reply.

At the NIH Parkinson Clinic the doctors noted an improvement in my condition. Even my blood pressure was a bit elevated from its usual alarmingly low level.

My friends in the Parkinsonian Society also noticed a glow about me and new energies, much of which I devoted to building the Society. Donna was of great help in this work. She soon assumed editorship of the Society newsletter and got it off to a good start. She also helped considerably in producing this book by encouraging me and editing as well as typing parts of the manuscript.

As was to be expected, some of my children had difficulty adjusting to the idea of a woman other than their mother sharing their father's love. But as they came to know Donna and to see the beneficial effects of our relationship, they, too, seemed to develop affection for her.

My old circle of friends continued to invite me and, later, my new companion to their social functions. They welcomed Donna graciously, even though it was sometimes obvious that Debbie's ghost was with us.

But as time went on, the difficulty of traveling twelve miles each way between our homes, the necessary separations for days at a time, and the disadvantages of having to care for an excessively large house began to make me think of moving.

At about the same time one of the doctors at the NIH Parkinson Clinic advised me to find a smaller residence in a more convenient location. He suggested I move to a ground-level apartment near transportation and shopping, while I was still able to cope with the move rather than risk the possibility of getting "stuck" because of an accident or advancing symptoms and having to make emergency arrangements.

I longed to marry again, but did not think it would be fair to burden Donna with the possibility of coping with the totally incapacitated invalid I might turn out to be. There were also problems of different kinds involving our children and perhaps she valued her independence after a first, unhappy marriage. And so, for the foreseeable future, we chose to live in separate households but close enough for easy access.

With Donna's help, and that of a very aggressive real estate agent, I found a condominium apartment that was "just what the doctor ordered," ground floor and all. It is big enough to put up family and friends when they visit and compact enough for easy care. In addition to being one block from a bus, it is two blocks from almost everything else: shopping, medical center, health club, swimming pool, parks, and fishing ponds. And most important, it is only one block from Donna.

Starting a new life in middle age is a scary thing even for a healthy person. For a parkinsonian it can be especially challenging, physically and emotionally. Making even tiny decisions about what to keep or give away in preparation for a move can immobilize one. Waves of depression washed over me, but the waves soon receded, probably because I rarely felt alone during the transition period. My children gathered from all over the country to help sort, pack, take away, give away, and store the tremendous amount of possessions that we had accumulated like pack rats in eleven rooms, a basement, attic, garage, under beds, and even under couches and chairs. I faced an enormous job, but somehow I was able to muster the strength to do what was necessary.

Donna helped after work and weekends. Her most generous contribution was to take a week off from her job to help me move and to set up my new apartment. She worked so hard that at the end of the week my new home looked as if it had been lived in for years. It felt that way, too. The neat, convenient, attractive living conditions added greatly to my feeling of well-being. But most important to my well-being has been the emotional support provided by Donna and by my family and friends.

The self-confidence instilled in me by Donna has enabled me to travel more than I thought possible and

to enjoy activities such as dancing, picnics, and hikes—
activities that I had begun to give up.

On January 1, 1982, Donna and I were married in the
beautiful courtyard of the Hotel Del Coronado, near
San Diego, California. The simple ceremony included
these words:

> We thank Thee for the power of human love to heal the
> wounds of our lives... May their love and mutual devotion
> deepen with the years and may their service to Thee and the
> community hallow this deepest of all human relationships.

Since our marriage, we have made spreading hope
and ideas about how to cope with parkinsonism our
major hobby and purpose in life.

An informal style of duet-dialogue with members of
support groups began even before our actual marriage.
The morning we got our license we went directly from
the courthouse to a meeting of a local Parkinson support group. Donna was asked, as she has been many
times since, why she would marry a known parkinsonian. She responded, "I am not marrying a parkinsonian. I am marrying Sid because of the special
qualities he has as a human being which have come to
enrich my life. At least we know what we face and that
we can handle it. Many people discover or acquire
worse ailments after they are married and are unprepared to deal with them."

And I tell at such meetings how I am still learning to
accept my limitations, to utilize my remaining abilities
to the utmost, and to achieve the ever-evasive optimum
adjustment for medical treatment and living habits.

Thus, despite the inevitable problems of life in
general and parkinsonism in particular, Donna and I are
able to enjoy each day as it comes and to anticipate the
future with hope.

SUMMARY

Tips for Coping with Parkinsonism

Tips for Coping with Parkinsonism

A FRIEND whom I visited in the hospital was so depressed that he had called his wife earlier that day and informed her that he was going to die and that he wanted to die. When I asked him why, he mentioned what seemed to me to be mildly advancing symptoms of parkinsonism.

"Joe," I told him, "I've experienced much worse. I've lived through it and I still enjoy life."

"Really?"

"Really."

For illustration, I read him portions of the manuscript for this book. As I read, he made comments such as: "You felt that way, too?" "I didn't know you had such trouble accepting parkinsonism, because now you seem at peace with it." "I feel better knowing you were able to survive some of the same things I'm suffering through now. I thought I was unique."

When I finished reading to him, he went to the phone, dialed his wife, and announced: "I'm not going to die after all."

Joe's spirits lifted when he realized that he was not alone in the world. It was a recognition that, although each person on earth is to a certain extent unique and each case of parkinsonism is different, people (including parkinsonians) are also alike—probably more alike than they are different. And he saw that one of those likenesses is that people are resilient.

173

Others with whom I have shared my experiences have commented that they were inspired by the feeling that "if you made it, I can too." And some were encouraged by the thought that they had handled it better than I had. Just as I have learned from the successes and mistakes of others, others can learn from my mistakes as well as from my achievements.

Probably, the most important messages for family members, and for medical personnel too, will be in the emotional realm. By reading how a patient *feels* about his ailment in the context of his total life, they may get a better *feel* for how to deal with parkinsonians.

Recognizing that each reader will interpret my experience differently depending on his background, I have nevertheless identified ten tips for coping with parkinsonism that I believe have rather universal application. These are addressed primarily to the patient, but they relate also to anyone who shares responsibility for the care and welfare of a parkinsonian.

Ten Tips for Coping with Parkinsonism

1. Learn all you can about parkinsonism and its treatment.
2. Choose a doctor carefully.
3. Become a partner in treatment.
4. Accept and accommodate to your limitations.
5. Make the most of your remaining abilities: Keep active.
6. Take care of your general health.
7. Find purpose in your life.
8. Reach out to help someone: Give and accept love.
9. Have fun.
10. Create your own miracle.

1. *Learning About Parkinsonism*

"I'm afraid to learn too much about parkinsonism. It's likely to be depressing," said a participant in a Parkinsonian Society discussion. That's a common attitude. But despite the dangers, Dr. Roger Duvoisin, who wrote the informative *Parkinson's Disease: A Manual for Patient and Family*, decided to "tell it like it is" because:

> It is obvious in practice that patients do better and can face their problems with equanimity and intelligence when they gain a reasonable understanding of their affliction, of what the doctor is trying to do for them, and of what can be done with treatments currently available.[1]

Duvoisin notes that in recent years treatment of parkinsonism has become more effective but also more complicated.

> Consequently, the success of treatment depends more than ever on the cooperation of the patient and the family. The best cooperation is built on intelligent understanding... but, alas! There is too little time in the daily bustle and rush of medical practice to explain all that needs explaining and to answer all the questions asked by every patient. Then, too, patients often think of the most important questions after they have left the doctor's office, and forget them by the time of the next visit. Some questions are difficult to ask, and perhaps the patient does not know how or what to ask. It is often preferable and easier to find the answers in private, in a book.[2]

Duvoisin's book is an excellent source of information. Other printed materials are available from the national organizations listed in the appendix of this volume. An especially informative newsletter is published quarterly by the United Parkinson Foundation.

[1] Roger C. Duvoisin, *Parkinson's Disease: A Guide for Patient and Family* (New York: Raven Press, 1978), p. *vii*.
[2] Ibid., p. *v*.

The same foundation sponsors patient information symposia several times a year in different parts of the country. At these sessions a panel of neurologists tells about the latest developments in treatment and answers questions from the audience. A growing number of local societies for parkinsonians and their families also sponsor various kinds of information programs.

In a local self-help organization you will also have an opportunity to share informally various strategies which patients and their families discover for coping with the "silent sickness." These strategies may range from matters considered too petty or embarrassing to discuss with a doctor, such as what kind of pajamas enable one to turn over easily in bed or what to do about sexual relations.

2. *Selecting a Physician*

Patients often ask: Should I go to a neurologist or will a general practitioner, family doctor, or internist do?

If you find a competent neurologist who will consider your total health, will give you enough time and attention, and to whom you can relate personally, this neurologist would be preferable to any other type of physician.

But if the available neurologists appear too busy to pay attention to the meticulous adjustments that need to be made in medication and to work out the petty problems faced by parkinsonians, or are not concerned about your total health, you may do better with a general practitioner.

By the time most people are affected with parkinsonism, they already are being treated for several other ailments of advancing age. And parkinsonism affects so many aspects of one's health, it is difficult to separate one symptom or treatment from another.

Thus, if you have good rapport with your present internist, general practitioner, family doctor, or geriatrics specialist, it might be best to continue with him, provided he has access to and will call upon a competent neurologist as consultant when necessary.

And, if you agree that the patient and his family should be partners in treatment, you should ascertain whether your prospective physician concurs.

3. Sharing Responsibility for Treatment

Don't try to be your own doctor, but help your doctor help you. You can assist in several ways:

One is to keep a medical diary—notes on what happens to you, what medications you take, and how you feel. Bring these notes and any questions, in writing, to your visit with the physician. Otherwise you may forget your most important observations or questions.

Be sure you understand what the doctor tells you. Before you leave his office, be sure you are perfectly clear on his instruction for treatment.

If you have any problems or questions between visits, don't wait three months for your next scheduled visit or decide on your own to change your dosage or other treatment. Call your doctor and discuss any problems between visits. Avoid, especially, the temptation to take more than the prescribed dosage of medication.

Family members should be involved as much as possible in conferences with physicians because the patient is often so emotionally charged that he does not remember much of what the doctor said or he interprets the doctor's words subjectively. The family member or friend can also help give the doctor a more objective and more complete picture of what has happened since the last visit.

The role of the family member or friend as patient advocate, intermediary, or interpreter is particularly important for the parkinsonian patient who finds it difficult to speak clearly or quickly enough to pose a question, concern, or suggestion when confronted by a busy doctor.

4. Accepting Limitations

Among the many parkinsonians I know, there is very little relationship between how happy a person is and his or her physical condition. Some who have only a slight tremor are bitter about their fate and continually ask "Why me?" Others, who are so debilitated they are confined to a wheelchair, are cheerful, gregarious, and concerned about others. What makes the difference?

The simple passage of time will help many people to accept their limitations as they get used to them. Some are fortunate to have the benefits of religious faith; love and support of family, friends, and health care personnel; a feeling of purpose in life; and the sheer enjoyment of living.

The way in which parkinsonians are first told they have the ailment is extremely important in determining how they will accept and accommodate to it the rest of their lives.

This is where the human relations skills of a physician come into play. The same facts can be stated in a way that instills either fear or relative security and hope.

Parkinsonians, when they talk with one another, usually recall almost the exact words and manner of the physician who first diagnosed their condition.

Here is how one former Army officer (Officer A) remembers his doctor's diagnosis:

You've got Parkinson's disease. It's a progressive malfunction of the nervous system and there's no cure for it. The average lifespan of parkinsonians after diagnosis is twelve years, but you'll be unfit for duty long before then. You'll get increasing tremor, stiffness, difficulty of movement, so you'd better start thinking about retirement.

Essentially the same facts were presented by another doctor to Army Officer B as follows:

You have a neurological condition in which your nerves have trouble controlling the muscles. Fortunately, the condition isn't very advanced. It's an ailment that usually progresses very slowly. Sometimes it even reaches a plateau and doesn't get any worse for a long time. You should be able to continue almost normal activities for the foreseeable future.

You won't need special medication at this point, but if your symptoms progress there are several drugs that can alleviate the tremor, stiffness, or slowness of movement that may develop. Although there is no permanent cure yet known, you are fortunate to be living at a time when so much progress is being made in treating parkinsonism that the outlook for at least controlling the symptoms is very good.

After describing the nature of the illness and its treatment in more detail, the second doctor took adequate time to answer the patient's questions and concluded the session with several suggestions regarding desirable health practices. He concluded: "Stay as active as you can. There is less danger of wearing out than of rusting out."

Of course, Officer B accepted and accommodated to his ailment much better than Officer A.

5. *Keeping Active*
There is a tendency among people who learn they

have a chronic illness to think: "I'll have to start taking it easy now."

That's usually not a good idea for parkinsonians. Instead, you should continue your old activities as long as you are able. This applies to nonphysical interests and skills as well as physical exercises. It's much easier to continue or to revive an old skill than to learn a new one.

We see this point demonstrated frequently at the summer camps of the Parkinsonian Society of Greater Washington. One of the participants who was so debilitated he normally couldn't get around without a wheelchair was inspired to try his old diving and swimming skills. He had someone wheel him to the diving board. It took him ten minutes to inch his way the length of the board, but he managed a creditable dive and swam across the Camp Maria pool. He did this twice in succession.

When we had dancing that evening he danced with seven different partners in a row. And when we told jokes he raised his normally inaudible mumble to a level loud and clear enough to be heard all over the recreation room.

If you are working for pay or are responsible for maintaining a household, try to carry out your work as long as possible. This is important not only to keep active but to keep purpose in your life. If necessary to extend your working career, consider taking less responsibility and less pay. Work as long as you can without building up excessive stress.

But if you are obviously unable to perform reasonably well, the sense of frustration and failure will outweigh the benefits of the work responsibility. When that happens, try to withdraw gracefully.

6. *Assuming Responsibility for Your General Health*

It amazes me to observe how many doctors and patients act as if parkinsonism and the medications taken for treatment can be isolated from the total workings of that complicated organism, the human body. One's total health and the factors contributing to health such as diet, exercise, rest, recreation, and emotional factors seem to me to be as important as medication in determining how well a patient will function. One of the clearest illustrations of this point occurs to me every morning.

I take the same dosage of medication at the same time upon arising each day. The doctors tell me it should take about half an hour for it to take effect. But that's just an average. Sometimes I can't seem to get mobile enough to walk from the bedroom to the kitchen for an hour. Sometimes I can get right up, stretch a few times, do a few minutes of mild exercise, and get going in ten or fifteen minutes.

What makes the difference? It depends on such things as how good a night's rest I've had, what I ate the day before, what kind of exercise I had, my state of relaxation or tension, and when I last moved my bowels.

These are all factors more within the control of the patient than anyone else. Therefore, I have tried— through trial and error, reading and discussions with doctors and other patients—to find which health routines work best for me.

Some of these routines relate especially to parkinsonism. For example, it is now well established that too much protein or vitamin B^6 interferes with the action of levodopa. But both are essential for good health. So one must work out a balanced diet that

provides enough nutrition without too much interference with one's medication.

On the other hand, certain principles of good nutrition affect everyone's health. An example is too much
sugar. Many parkinsonians I know have a craving for
sweets but feel much better if they can resist it.

I shall not attempt to detail here the specific diets,
exercises, or types of recreation that might be especially good for parkinsonians. There are other sources of
information about these listed in the appendix, and
each individual must work out his own needs and
practices.

The important messages here are: Only you can
control your own general health. It takes a lot of
attention to a lot of details, and much self-control, but
it's worth it if you want to live as full a life as possible.

7. Finding Purpose in Your Life

Holding a job or taking care of a household automatically gives a sense of purpose to most people. If you
give these up, you should replace them with other
purposeful activities.

One person may find planning and maintaining a
garden to be a major purpose in his life. Another may
need to make some impact on the intellectual world.
Others find purpose in extending love and help to
their families. Some reach out to help others who
share their plight or who are worse off than they are.

Giving purpose to your life does not necessarily
mean achieving some grand objective. It is psychologically satisfying to complete some achievable tasks,
however simple, each day. Be specific and realistic in
your goals and then take pride in your achievement.
This is better than struggling to complete a task with
no end. For example, it is better to say to your spouse,

"Today I'm going to plant six rose bushes," rather than, "Today I'm going to fix up the garden as much as possible."

8. Reaching Out

If you reach out to help someone else, you will be helping yourself. You can do this individually and through organizations.

The value of a local organization for people sharing the same problem is illustrated in the following excerpt from a letter by the wife of a parkinsonian, a middle-aged man who had begun to withdraw from life:

> In the summer of 1978 we were invited to go to Camp Maria with the Parkinsonian Society of Greater Washington. We met some very badly handicapped people who turned out to be the most beautiful people in the world. The first day we met these lovely people, we felt like we had known them all our lives. We found love, joy, patience, and kindness in everything they did. There was no problem in anything they did for you. You could feel the warmth and love they had for each other. One day I heard one of our friends tell another buddy he was almost glad he had Parkinson's disease because he met so many wonderful people, and he was experiencing another whole new way of life. The whole world looked different to him now. I have learned that being handicapped enriches your life.
>
> When it came time to go home, we shared in laughter, tears, hugs, kisses, and love for each other. They made us feel like we were the most important people in the world. What a wonderful experience it was.

The therapeutic effects of love—given and received—have been described several times in earlier chapters. Dr. Oliver Sacks says it even more strongly. He writes ". . . the work of healing, of rendering whole, is first and last, the business of Love."[3]

---

[3]Oliver Sacks, *Awakenings* (Garden City, NY: Doubleday & Co., 1974), p. 234.

The implications of Sacks's statement for medical personnel are quite controversial. Some health-care professionals bend over backwards to keep from getting emotionally involved with patients and thus are so cold the patient feels like a thing, not a person, and becomes depressed. Other health-care personnel show their concern for their patients so clearly the patient feels much better knowing that someone cares, but the professional gets so emotionally involved that his or her effectiveness is adversely affected.

Happily, there is a middle ground. It is possible, without getting emotionally involved, to smile at a patient, touch him or her reassuringly and take a few minutes of conversation to show you care about him as a person. That's the mark of a true professional.

The spouse, child, or friend or relative who is already "emotionally involved" often hesitates to tell or show his affection for a chronically ill person. If this description applies to you, try reaching out and touching the person you love verbally and physically. One effect may be to reduce the family medicine bill.

Contrary to the fears of some parkinsonians and their spouses, I can attest that onset of the ailment does not necessarily mean the end of romantic interest or sexual capability, especially for those on levodopa or other modern medications. In fact, levodopa and perhaps bromocriptine seem to increase my libido.

9. Having Fun

"Children, how can you laugh and joke when grandma feels so poorly?" I once heard the daughter of a parkinsonian say to her own youngsters.

"But we're trying to cheer up grandma," the nine-year old replied. "Is that bad?"

Of course, it's not bad. Almost any kind of fun or

pleasure will have a positive effect on a parkinsonian, or anyone else for that matter. But many spouses and other family members, in their zeal to do "the right thing" by the stricken family member, maintain a somber atmosphere that is bad for patient and those around him.

Some enjoyable activities should be planned for the patient each day. And a person who cares for a parkinsonian should also take some time for himself or herself. Family members should not feel guilty about taking a break from the parkinsonian, even if the patient expresses displeasure at being left alone or with someone else. For if the spouse or other family member doesn't get some rest and recreation, eventually his or her own health and/or attitude will be so adversely affected the patient will suffer more than from periodic separations.

"I haven't been out of earshot of my husband for a month," a wife of a parkinsonian once proudly told me.

Instead of praising her, my reply was: "Don't be a martyr. It's important to him as well as you to get some relief each day and periodically for longer times. Your husband is better off with a happy, healthy gadabout than with a nagging martyr."

Laughing *is* good medicine in itself and it enhances the effectiveness of the chemical medicines.

Have you ever noticed that the most successful doctors, nurses, social workers, and chaplains are often those who can get a patient to laugh, or at least smile? They often break the tension by telling a joke on themselves.

Psychologists of humor tell us that there are narrow lines dividing humor from fear, embarrassment, or shock. The way one perceives or describes an incident can determine whether it is humorous, and thus relieves stress; or embarrassing, fearful, or shocking, and thus creates stress.

There are many incidents in the life of a parkinsonian, such as being mistaken for a drunk, that can be used either to sour one's disposition, or to give one something to laugh about. Swapping stories of humorous incidents is an activity that almost all parkinsonians can enjoy.

Some brave souls have learned to laugh at themselves even in the face of death. One morning shortly after a friend had undergone extremely critical surgery, I asked him how he was feeling. "Well," he replied, "I had such a bad time last night that this morning I decided to end it all so I wouldn't be such a burden to my wife and others. I tried to hold my breath until I expired. I must have turned all colors, but try as hard as I could, it didn't work. So, I gathered what remaining breath I had left and hollered 'HELP!' as loud as I could. When a nurse surprised me by showing up immediately," he said with a chuckle, "I took it as a good omen and decided to give life another try."

10. Creating Miracles

When levodopa first proved valuable as a medication for treating parkinsonism, it was sometimes referred to as a "miracle drug." As adverse long-term side effects have emerged in many patients, and the limitations of the drug have become better known and understood, the term "miracle drug" is now seldom used.

So much research on the mechanism and treatment of parkinsonism has been conducted during the past few decades that it is realistic to expect another significant research breakthrough in the future. This knowledge should give hope to all parkinsonians for improved treatment in their lifetimes. But we should not sit around waiting for "*the* miracle drug" to be discovered. For if we apply more carefully and completely what is already known about treating and coping with parkinsonism, the quality of life could be improved for many parkinsonians right now. By cooperative action of patient, family and friends, and medical personnel, we can make our own miracles!

A Patient's View:
Is It Worth It?

Shortly after my book *Parkinson's: A Patient's View*, was published in 1981, Lorraine Pecarsky, a young woman who had interviewed me for a feature story, telephoned to ask a poignant question:

> In reviewing my notes on your book and our interview I'm impressed with the tremendous effort it takes for you to cope with your parkinsonism. You have to remember to take your medicine nine times a day, you write down the variations in your condition, you are careful with your diet, you have to exercise, you have to cope with side effects of your medication, you have to plan and time almost everything you do, and so on. It takes so much effort to live. Is it worth it?

"Of course I believe it is. That's why I wrote the book," was my reply. "But," I quickly added, "I won't know for sure until five to ten years from now."

Seven years have passed since I made that comment. In those years, Donna (whom I married one month after the book was published) and I have spoken to forty Parkinson audiences in thirty-five cities across the continent on the theme of my book—"Accommodation Without Surrender." At such meetings we are closely scrutinized and discreetly questioned to see how I am doing in regard to my Parkinson symptoms, and what medicine I am taking.

Audiences want to know from Donna how she remains so cheerful and how she fights off caretaker's burnout. And, increasingly, we have been receiving such questions as:

> So much has happened in Parkinson research treatment, and Parkinson organizations since your book was first published in 1981. What would you say are the most important developments? How would they affect the philosophy and content of your book if you were to rewrite it today? What has happened to you two during the last seven years?

To answer these questions fully would require another book. Nonetheless, to be brief, our experiences of the past seven years support the validity of the coping techniques promulgated in *Parkinson's*. Its major theme remains as applicable today as when I first framed it. It works, especially the "Ten Tips," particularly when we are persistent at following our philosophy.

If I were writing my book today, I wouldn't change its content philosophy. There have been no new findings or developments that reduce the need for achieving a delicate balance in medication and lifestyle and for maintaining positive attitudes. Neither has there been any major breakthrough directly resulting in cure or easy elimination of Parkinson symptoms.

New Developments

A number of important developments have occurred in the Parkinson world during the 1980s. These include:

- Movement to shift greater responsibility to patients for their own health.
- Phenomenal growth of Parkinson support groups.
- Growing access to information about parkinsonism.

- Expanded research on the brain in general and parkinsonism in particular.
- Improved delivery of medical care to Parkinson patients.

These developments have occured in conjunction with the the emergence since 1981 of Parkinson or Movement Disorder Centers. These centers, which number in the dozens, combine diagnosis and treatment of patients; research; and the dissemination of information to patients, the public, and health-care professionals.

The centers offer the Parkinsonian the advantage of being able to shift easily from being a regular patient to being an experimental patient and back again when the experimental protocol is completed. It takes about five years to get a new drug approved for general use after it has been tested for safety and effectiveness on animals and a small number of humans. Many of us can't wait five years. Often the apparent benefits seem to outweigh the long-term risks and possible side effects. These centers offer a compromise.

Another advantage of the centers is that researchers have a convenient source of pre-screened, potential human test subjects. Even if the patient isn't interested in participating in research studies, the centers provide an opportunity to be diagnosed and/or treated by clinical neurologists who are knowledgeable and interested in the latest developments in the treatment of parkinsonism. The patient also receives comprehensive coordinated care by a team of neurologists, internists, specially trained nurses, therapists, and social workers.

Usually patients are referred to the centers by their doctors for confirmation of diagnosis and/or initiation of a treatment plan. A dramatic example of the effectiveness of these centers is that from one-quarter to one-third of the patients referred to them are found to have been incorrectly diagnosed. Either their Parkinson's condition was not identified as such or another ailment was thought to be Parkinson's.

The Parkinson Center, however, does not eliminate the need for patients to get comprehensive continuing care from a general practitioner, internist, or gerontologist.

Applying What We Know

It was just such a center that was responsible in 1988 for my fourth dramatic "rescue" from the ravages of parkinsonism. This time it was not a new experimental drug that did the trick. It was the full application of what is already known about the treatment of parkinsonism that worked.

The medical team reviewed my complicated medical history carefully and found that there were a few combinations of commonly used medications that somehow I had missed during more than two decades of treatment. They added one major drug and together we juggled the amounts and timing of all my medications for several months until a temporary optimum was reached.

It was not all a matter of drugs—psychological factors contributed as well. The center staff helped give me a new purpose in life by recruiting Donna and me to write a series of essays for a patient information service at Graduate Hospital. Because of the security of my marriage and my confidence in the medical team, I was motivated to renew my attention to the nitty-gritty details that when taken together make a big difference in one's condition. I was moved to reread my own book and to note where I had slipped in the path I had mapped out for others. Both Donna and I redoubled our efforts to practice what we preached. And it worked!

Lest I give the impression that I am about to train for the Olympics, I hasten to add that I'm still severely handicapped compared to a normal 63-year old. But considering the nearly thirty years I have endured the ailment and compared to five to ten years ago, I'm doing remarkably well.

Remarkable Improvement

I use the term "remarkable" literally. Ever since my book was published there has been a flood of remarks assessing my condition. These began with the little girls in my neighborhood who remarked upon seeing me walk when very dyskinetic, "Look how funny that man walks!" And, noting how the little dog I was walking jumped frantically from one side to the other as I jerked her leash uncontrollably, another child remarked, "And his dog walks funny too!"

Adults made comments, also. For example, when Donna and I arrived at the Ford Auditorium to give our dual presentation in Detroit six years ago, one gentleman in the audience looked us up and down as we entered the building and said to me very candidly, "You don't look as good as I expected."

Recently when we returned to speak to the same organization we were told by almost everyone who had seen us before, including Mr. Candid, "You look and sound better than you did five years ago."

My improved condition was no cosmetic or sartorial feat. There were several major objective indications of a reversal of symptoms. Most obvious was the almost complete absence of dyskinesia.

Another change was in my weight. For several years I had steadily lost weight, going from 160 to 128 pounds. In 1988, I gained more than ten pounds. I feel and look calmer most of the time. And I'm able to walk more often and further than before.

A walk to the shopping center one recent day moved me to the verge of tears of joy. The little girl—who had made the comment "...his dog walks funny, too!"— now a teenager, said to me "I'm happy to see how much better you're walking." As I walked on, three other people stopped to tell me how much better I appeared to be. "Did you have brain surgery?" asked one. "Is there a new medicine for your condition?" asked another.

When I reached the shopping center one of the maintenance men, who I didn't know had ever noticed me, said, "You're walking so much better now. Did you know that?" I was too choked up to reply.

Now I walk not only for the health of it, but also for the joy of it. After so many years of struggling to cover ground one way or another, mostly another, it is a thrill just to feel a smoother stride.

Among many other improvements, one of the most important is a stronger voice and the ability to communicate more readily and completely. "I'm surprised, I heard every word you said clearly," my 85-year old mother told me after one long-distance call to her.

In June of 1988, Donna and I reached a pinnacle of success in accommodating without surrender when we went on a two week trip to England. We planned it carefully care with the help of British pen pals and the Parkinson's Disease Society of the United Kingdom. We completed an extremely active trip with no difficulty. And we collected more evidence that coping with parkinsonism—the hard way—is worth it.

It Takes Patience and Persistence

If I were writing *Parkinson's: A Patient's View* today, I would surely want to inform my readers about the new experiments underway, such as those being conducted with fetal cell implants. But, most importantly, I would want to convey the simple message that despite these experiments, the immediate prospect of alleviation of Parkinson symptoms remains much greater by applying more fully, with patience and persistence, what is already known about the treatment of the disorder.

I can now say, without hesitation, "Yes, Lorraine, it is worth it!"

Sidney Dorros
May 1989

A Spouse's View: Yes, It's Worth It!

There have been a lot of ups and downs since Sid and I were married in 1981 and his book was published. We have shared the misery of broken bones—both of us at approximately the same time. We have endured at least four experimental drug trials that had less-than-hoped-for results. We have suffered the loss of a number of close friends and relatives. We have coped with a variety of problems with our respective children that were, at times, stressful. We have dealt with medical crises that were potentially life-threatening. We have accepted the need for the use of a wheelchair at times. Sid has adjusted to the fact that it is no longer safe for him to drive a car. But through it all, we have never let what was going on in our lives prevent us from keeping our commitment to speak before any Parkinson group when asked. Sometimes we were in casts and sometimes in wheelchairs. At one memorable meeting in Englewood, New Jersey, we *both* arrived in wheelchairs.

It has not been all gloom and doom. We learned to hone our skills in speaking, writing, and laughing about the plights in which we sometimes found ourselves. We have completed forty trips around the United States, Canada, and Great Britain to speak before Parkinson's groups or medical conferences. Most of all, we have learned that Sid's tips of coping really do work.

We Practice What We Preach

In 1987, Sid's parkinsonism and side effects from drugs had gotten to the point that for only about 5 percent of each day was he not dyskinetic or rigid. It was at that time we decided we should practice more fully what we preach. We had been recommending to groups all over the country that they try the comprehensive approach offered at Parkinson Centers. The one we were most familiar with was about one hundred miles away. We decided it would be worth it to travel the distance, if Sid's condition could be improved.

Today I get great joy telling people that Sid is doing better than he has at any time since 1980. The explanation for his improved condition is not a simple one because it is due to many factors or changes. First, we redoubled our efforts to accomplish a delicate balance in his diet, exercise regime, and sleep, and we also worked to reduce stress in our lives. Second, we completed a careful titration of his various medications—adding some, dropping others, adjusting amounts and frequency—and that certainly helped. But, most importantly, it was a renewed purpose in Sid's life that brought about his improvement.

Specifically, the purpose sprang from a series of individual essays that we worked on together to put in a data bank for use by both patients and caregivers. But, in a greater sense, it came from practicing what we preach.

Working with the Doctor

We can't overlook how important the comprehensive approach to treatment has been for Sid and the mutual respect that has developed between the medical

team and us. We made a determined effort to be partners in Sid's treatment. It was, in fact, this partner-
ship that led to a crucial discovery.

Before going to the center for his first visit, Sid had
put his entire twenty-seven-year medication history on
his computer. It was this history that enabled the nurse
practitioner to make an important discovery. She identified a Parkinson drug that Sid had never taken. The
addition of this medicine has contributed substantially
to his improvement.

For each visit, Sid now comes prepared with a
printout of what medication he has been taking, when,
how much, and detailing any problems he has
experienced. He also prepares a list of questions and
concerns he might have developed since the last visit.
I am at his side throughout the examination and discussion with the doctor. I believe it is important for
spouses to be an advocate in communication with the
doctor and to take notes of any changes or special
instructions.

Sid's tips for coping that we found to be so effective
for patients can be applied equally to the caregiver.
The most important one of all is for both the caregiver
and the patient—learn to accept and accommodate
Parkinson's in their lives. You will find that through
accommodation you can find a winning approach
to life.

Caregivers Have Needs Too
You will find it critical to your own health and happiness to keep as active as your partner's condition will
permit. Keep up your social contacts and outside interests. Plan some special time for yourself as often as you
can, to do things that you enjoy. Go out to lunch with

friends, visit museums and art galleries, go shopping just for yourself. Only you know what gives you the most pleasure. Whether your partner wants you to go or not, you will find you both benefit. Upon your return, you will be recharged and your spouse can share your experience vicariously.

Hopefully, along the way you have kept your sense of how to have fun. Life need not always be grim. We all still have a little child in each of us that allows for pleasures to be gained from a variety of experiences. Both patient and caregiver need to have fun, together and separately.

Being responsible for your own general health is also essential because you are the only one who can "give care to this caregiver, while the caregiver is busy giving care." This, of course, means more than just general health. You, too, must have a goal or purpose in your life. For me, as well as for Sid, speaking to and writing for parkinsonians and their caregivers have given us a wonderful sense of purpose. But in addition to that, I have found that developing an interest completely apart from Sid's ailment is important also. Fulfilling a long-standing desire to become involved in genealogical research has provided me a with a consuming and satisfying pastime.

Everyone is different, though, and you are the only one who can identify what would best satisfy you.

Find or Form a Support Group

One form of work that gives more than a sense of purpose is to volunteer with your own local support group. If you don't have a group, start one. Interacting with others in the same life situation can be rewarding as a way of reaching out and helping someone else. It can also be a way of giving and accepting love. We have met people who find this kind of activity to be so enriching that they have reached out to do other volunteer work as well. In Minneapolis, Minnesota, a couple told us they regularly attend and work with three different groups. They have found it has become an important part of their lives and feel that they have received as much as they give. Sid and I have certainly found this to be true in that we have learned from others as much as we have imparted to them.

The coordinator of a medical program that we were part of several years ago in Providence, Rhode Island, said something to us that we shall never forget. I pass it along to all of you who read this with the hope that you can apply it in your own lives. He said that by the time most of us have reached forty or so we have had to deal with some kind of major problem in our lives. The trick is to wear your "crown of thorns" cocked jauntily over one eye!

Another memorable person that we met on that trip was a Parkinsonian who said, "Shucks, 'taint nothing at all, but 'taint easy." With an attitude like that, you can create your own miracles. It won't be easy, but with patience and persistence it is possible.

Donna Dorros
May 1989

What Is Parkinsonism?

The following basic information about parkinsonism is excerpted from a pamphlet prepared by the National Institute of Neurological and Communicative Disorders and Stroke, The NINCDS Research Program: Parkinson's Disease, 1980. (In 1988, the NINCDS' name was changed to the National Institute of Neurological Disorders and Stroke (NINDS).)

Parkinson's disease is one of the most severely crippling disorders of the nervous system and one of the most common among older people. The disease afflicts an estimated 1 in 1,000 in the general population—and 1 in 100 in the population over age 60.

Cardinal symptoms of Parkinson's disease are uncontrollable tremor of the extremities, muscle rigidity, and difficulty in initiating movement. Depression often accompanies these motor disturbances.

As the disorder progresses, the typical patient develops stooped posture, loss of facial expression, a shuffling gait, and increasing difficulty in walking, talking, writing, and performing other actions that require a high degree of muscular coordination. Depression may worsen, and there may be severe mental deficits.

Without treatment, the average patient is severely disabled within 5 to 10 years of the disorder's onset, but some patients have had mild cases for 20 and even 30 years. While Parkinson's disease itself is rarely the primary cause of death, it often so weakens its victims that they fall prey to other illnesses.

Cause

An estimated seven out of every eight patients who show signs of parkinsonism have the primary or "idiopathic" form of the disorder—Parkinson's disease itself—the cause of which is still unknown. (A small number of patients with parkinsonian symptoms have what is termed "secondary parkinsonism," which may be precipitated by adverse reactions to certain drugs given for other illnesses, or may follow viral infection. Symptoms may also appear in connection with certain other neurological disorders, and occasionally may result from vascular disease or exposure to such toxic agents as manganese or carbon monoxide.)

While much about primary parkinsonism remains obscure, a great deal has been learned about its effects—particularly within the brain itself. Patients with Parkinson's disease have a striking deficiency of dopamine—a chemical substance necessary for transmission of nerve impulses—in a region of the brain (the basal ganglia) concerned with control and regulation of movement. On postmortem examination, brain tissue from Parkinson's disease patients shows marked loss of dopamine—containing nerve cells particularly in the substantia nigra, a normally dark area that may look almost white in the brains of severely affected patients.

Researchers do not yet know why these cells die— or, indeed, why these particular cells are singled out for attack. Hypotheses now under investigation include infection by an unconventional viral agent, exposure to environmental toxins, breakdown of the body's protective mechanisms with advancing age, and unexplained acceleration of the normal aging process.

Treatment

Though the first systematic description of Parkinson's disease (London physician James Parkinson's *Essay on the Shaking Palsy*) appeared in 1817, it was not until the last quarter of the 19th century that a treatment of even limited usefulness emerged. Extracts from the belladonna plant were found to be of some help in relaxing stiffened muscles and quieting tremors, and were used in therapy until after World War II, when a number of similarly acting synthetic drugs came into use.

Discovery of the brain dopamine deficiency in parkinsonian patients—reported in 1960 by researchers at the University of Vienna—brought hope that restoring the dopamine level might effectively treat the disease. Investigators soon found, however, that giving dopamine itself was useless: the substance did not reach the brain because it could not cross the blood-brain barrier, a protective biochemical mechanism by which the body screens agents passing from the blood into the central nervous system.

Scientists then turned to levodopa, the substance that is dopamine's metabolic precursor, last link in a chain of chemical reactions leading to production of dopamine. Levodopa *did* cross the blood-brain barrier and could be quickly metabolized into dopamine. After extensive trials in many medical centers, levodopa (or L-Dopa) was approved for prescription sale in 1970.

Some early problems with levodopa occurred because the drug is broken down very rapidly in the body, requiring large doses if the substance is to penetrate to the brain. In some patients, toxic side effects from these dose levels were so severe that the drug had to be discontinued. Investigators learned, however, that they could greatly reduce dose levels— and thus cut down on some side effects—by giving levodopa in conjunction with a substance that slows its breakdown in the body. A drug known as Sinemet—combining levodopa and the inhibiting substance carbidopa—has been available on prescription since 1975.

For the Parkinson's disease patient the levodopa/carbidopa combination still stands as the single most effective therapy available. Most patients benefit from it: some moderately, some with striking relief from their symptoms—at least for several years. But the drug seems to become less effective with long-term use, and it does not stay progression of the disease. Moreover, after using levodopa successfully for several years many patients develop disturbing problems that some scientists believe may be effects of the drug itself. One of the most distressing of these problems is the "on-off" reaction: abrupt fluctuation from states of normal function to states of near immobility or abnormal involuntary movement.

To delay development of such problems, a number of investigators now believe that less potent drugs should be given patients only mildly affected by the disease, and that levodopa should be withheld until its use becomes really necessary—i.e., when the illness has reached a stage where it threatens the patient's livelihood, domestic life, or psychological status. These scientists emphasize that levodopa will not be less effective when finally used, and hold that it should be employed when the need is greatest.

Clearly, though levodopa has been a boon to many patients, the search for an optimal treatment must proceed.

Research: New Drugs

. . . Scientists are testing new drugs developed as a result of expanded knowledge of the brain's biochemistry. The basal ganglia—the region of the brain most affected in parkinsonism—are now known to possess many complex and intricate biochemical circuits and to contain not only dopamine but several other neurotransmitters whose roles are not fully known. Moreover, the action of dopamine itself has been found to be far more complicated than was originally envisioned

Scientists now believe that there are two distinct categories of dopamine receptors—specific sites on "receiver" nerve cells to which dopamine delivers its "message" from the "sender" neurons. One category of receptor, labeled D-1, is linked to the enzyme adenylate cyclase. The other category, labeled D-2, acts independently of that enzyme.

Drugs that improve the symptoms of parkinsonism seem to mimic the action of dopamine at D-2 receptors, while drugs that induce or worsen parkinsonian symptoms seem to act as antagonists to dopamine at the same receptors. One focus of current efforts, therefore, is synthesis and testing of dopamine "agonists" (mimickers of dopamine) that will act selectively on the D-2 receptors. Unlike levodopa, which must undergo enzymatic conversion to dopamine before it can act on the receptors, the dopamine agonists act directly. Thus they may have more consistent therapeutic effects, and could continue to operate even if the enzymatic machinery needed to convert levodopa to dopamine were destroyed. Also, treatment with an agonist targeted specifically for the D-2 receptors, scientists theorize, might avert side effects linked to the more generalized actions of dopamine.

One of the first dopamine agonists to be tested was bromocriptine—a drug that has been studied for several years at NINCDS and elsewhere. The drug may be given alone, but is usually used as an adjunct to levodopa, in which case the dosage of the latter is reduced. Bromocriptine has been found to have at least limited usefulness, particularly in alleviating adverse reactions in patients who have had prolonged levodopa therapy. Its effectiveness, like that of levodopa, seems to lessen with time, however, and it can produce undesirable psychiatric reactions (reversible when the drug is withdrawn). . . .

Still more compounds, with various modes of action, await screening in laboratories around the country. All in all, what is most encouraging about today's search for a better drug therapy is that it is no longer a quixotic quest for a "miracle drug," but a search undertaken on a rational basis. As such, it holds much greater promise of success.

How Does It Feel To Be Parkinsonian?

Spouses, relatives, friends, and medical personnel who wish to help patients cope with the "silent sickness" need to understand what it *feels* like to be parkinsonian. But they are hindered because it is often difficult for the patient to come to terms with and then describe his feelings. At times, the ailment can undermine the patient's attempt to speak clearly; the condition is such that the patient may not be certain whether the problems of communication are physical or emotional. However, the late Margaret Bourke-White eloquently expressed herself by writing. Addressing herself to those who do not have the condition, she used words such as "surprise," "bewilderment," "awkwardness," and "panic" to describe her feelings.

> . . . to know what Parkinsonism is you must know the surprise of finding yourself standing in a sloping position as though you were trying to impersonate the leaning tower of Pisa. You must know the bewilderment of finding yourself prisoner in your own clothes closet, unable to back out of it. You must experience the awkwardness of trying to turn around in your own kitchen—eleven cautious little steps when one swift pivot used to do the job. You must live with the near panic which you face when you have to walk into a roomful of people, and the uneasiness of the questions you ask yourself: Do I just imagine that I can't seem to turn over

in bed any more? How will I get my feet moving when they
want to stay glued to the floor? How will I disengage myself
from a group of people and step away if they're all around
me? How will I keep from knocking them down? What can I
do with my hands when I'm only standing still?[1]

Bourke-White's description of what it feels like to
experience the symptoms of Parkinson's disease was
written before the advent of levodopa and other new
medications. Currently, someone like me in an advanced stage of the ailment, but who is benefitting
(and suffering side effects) from the new medications
can add words such as "joyful" and "euphoria" when
describing how it feels to be parkinsonian. Although I
still have occasional periods of stiffness, dyskinesia
caused by long-term use of strong doses of Sinemet
and bromocriptine is most disturbing to me.

Imagine the embarrassment of eating in a restaurant
while you are dyskinetic. With great concentration,
you are able to order your muscles to begin to cut your
steak; but as you finish the cut, the hand and arm
holding the knife seem to escape your control. Your
hand shoots out wildly, flinging a piece of pink meat
onto the lap of your dinner partner.

Or picture yourself trying to walk while dyskinetic
and experience the frustration of finding yourself, like
a newborn colt, kicking your feet high in the air, or
going sideways, or backwards—anyplace but the direction in which you are trying to go.

To understand what parkinsonism is like under
modern treatment, you must also experience the euphoria that comes each time your medicine does work
to relieve your stiffness. You must experience the
tickle of ecstasy that travels through your spine as

---

[1]Margaret Bourke-White, *Portrait of Myself* (New York, Simon & Schuster, 1963), p. 363.

your frozen-stiff body seems to thaw out. First you are able to move your fingers, then your wrists and arms, and finally, you can stand, stretch, and walk forward. When your left foot points out at the normal angle and you are able to stride out in large, rapid steps, you want to shout joyfully to the world, "Look, I can walk!"

And to know what it is like to be parkinsonian, you must know how it feels when, a few minutes later, a young child notices your increasing dyskinesia and calls out, "Mister, why are you walking so funny?"

APPENDIX III

Useful publications

Books about Parkinson's

Parkinson's at your fingertips, by Professor Adrian Williams and Dr Marie Oxtoby, published by Class Publishing

Parkinson's Disease: a guide for the patient and his family, by R.C. Duvoisin, published by Raven Press (USA)

Parkinson's Disease by Dr Harvey Sagar, published by Optima

Books by and about people with Parkinson's

Living Well with Parkinson's, by G. Wotton Attwood with L. Green Hunnewell, published by John Wiley & Sons Ltd.

Ray of Hope, by Andrew Lees and Ray Kennedy, published by Pelham Books

Publications for carers

Caring at Home, by Nancy Kohner, commissioned by the King's Fund Centre Carers Unit and published by the National Extension College, 18 Brooklands Avenue, Cambridge CB2 2NH

Taking a Break, published by the King's Fund Carers Unit (single copy free to carers available from Taking a Break, Newcastle-upon-Tyne X, NE85 2AQ)

What to look for in a Private or Voluntary Registered Home, published by Counsel and Care, Lower Ground Floor, Twyman House, 16 Bonny Street, London NW1 9PG (Tel: 0171 485 1566)

Taking Time for Me: How Caregivers Can Deal Effectively with Stress, by K.L. Karr, published by Prometheus Books

Coping with Dementia: a Handbook for Carers, published by Health Education Board Scotland, Woodburn House, Canaan Lane, Edinburgh EH10 4SG (Tel: 0131 536 5500) (Single copies are available free from local Health Boards in Scotland. People from outside Scotland can purchase copies – please telephone first to check the cost)

Caring for the Person with Dementia, by Bob Woods and Chris Lay, published by the Alzheimer's Disease Society, 10 Greencoat Place, London SW1P 1PH (Tel: 0171 306 0606) (There is a charge for this publication, but the Society also publishes a number of useful free leaflets, which are available directly from them or from their local branches)

Age Concern Factsheet Number 22: Legal Arrangements for Managing Financial Affairs (separate versions for England and Wales and for Scotland available from the relevant Age Concern offices at the addresses in Appendix 4)

Clothing and useful equipment

Advice Notes for People with Parkinson's Disease (resource paper), published jointly by the Disabled Living Foundation and the Parkinson's Disease Society (obtainable from the Parkinson's Disease Society)

Clothing for People with Parkinson's Disease, published

by Disability Scotland (obtainable free of charge from the Parkinson's Disease Society)

Equipment for an Easier Life, published by RICA (Research Institute for Consumer Affairs), 2 Marylebone Road, London NW1 4DF (single copies available free of charge on receipt of an A5 SAE)

Keep Able Mail Order Catalogue, obtainable free of charge from Keep Able Ltd at the address given in Appendix 4

The Special Collection (a mail order catalogue of fashion clothing selected for people with dressing difficulties), obtainable free of charge from J.D. Williams, Freepost, PO Box 123, Manchester M99 1BN (Tel: 0161 237 1200)

Sources of Information and Help

Age Concern England
Astral House
1268 London Road
London SW16 4ER
Tel: 0181 679 8000

Age Concern Scotland
113 Rose Street
Edinburgh EH3 9PT
Tel: 0113 232 4000

British Complementary
  Medicine Association
249 Fosse Road South
Leicester LE3 1AE
Tel: 0116 282 5511

British Society of Dentistry for
  the Handicapped
c/o Sue Greening
Dental Department
Town Center Clinic
Caradoc Road
Cwmbran
Gwent NP44 1XG
Tel: 01633 838356

Canon Communicators
Canon UK Ltd
Canon House
Manor Road
Wallington
Surrey SM6 0AJ
Tel: 0181 773 6000

Carers National Association
20/25 Glasshouse Yard
London EC1A 4JS
Tel: 0171 490 8818
Helpline: 0345 573 369 (10am–
  12am, 2pm–4pm weekdays)

Chivers Large Print Books
Chivers Press Ltd
Windsor Bridge Road
Bath BA2 3AX
Tel: 01225 335336

Continence Advisory Service
  Helpline
Tel: 0191 213 0050 (2pm–7pm
  weekdays)

Continence Foundation
2 Doughty Street
London WC1N 2PH
Tel: 0171 404 6875

Disabled Living Centers Council
Winchester House
11 Cranmer Road
Kennington Park
London SW9 6EJ
Tel: 0171 820 0567

Disability Sport England
13 Brunswick Place
London N1 6DX
Tel: 0171 490 4919

DVLA
(Driver and Vehicle Licensing
  Agency)
Drivers' Medical Unit
Longview Road
Morriston
Swansea SA99 1TU
Tel: 01792 783686

Gardening for the Disabled Trust
c/o F Seton
The Freight
Cranbrook
Kent TN17 3PG
Tel: 01580 712196

General Council and Register of
  Osteopaths
56 London Street
Reading
Berkshire RG1 4SQ
Tel: 01889 576585

Health Education Authority
Hamilton House
Mabledon Place
London WC1H 9TX
Tel: 0171 388 3833

Holiday Care Service
2nd Floor
Imperial Buildings
Victoria Road
Horley
Surrey RH6 7PX
Tel: 01293 774535

Institute for Complementary
  Medicine
PO Box 194
London SE16 1QZ
Tel: 0171 237 5165

Keep Able Ltd
For a mail order catalogue, write to:
Keep Able Ltd
FREEPOST
Wellingborough
Northants NN8 6BR
Shops at:
11/17 Kingston Road
Staines
Middlesex TW18 4QX
Tel: 01784 440044
and
Sterling Park
Pedmore Road
Brierley Hill
West Midlands DY5 1TB
Tel: 01384 484544
and
Fleming Close
Park Farm
Wellingborough
Northants NO 6UF
Tel: 01933 679 426

Motability
Goodman House
Station Approach
Harlow
Essex CM20 2ET
Tel: 01279 635666

Parkinson's Association of
  Ireland
Carmichael House
North Brunswick Street
Dublin 7
Ireland
Tel: 00353 1 872 2234 (from
  UK)

Parkinson's Disease Society
  (PDS)
National Office
22 Upper Woburn Place
London WC1H ORA
Tel: 0171 383 3515
Helpline: 0171 388 5798

Parkinson's Disease Society
  Brain Research Centre
1 Wakefield Street
London WC1N 1PJ
Tel: 0171 837 8370

RADAR
(Royal Association for Disability
  and Rehabilitation)
12 City Forum
250 City Road
London EC1V 8AF
Tel: 0171 250 3222

Relate National Marriage
  Guidance
Herbert Gray College
Little Church Street
Rugby
Warwickshire CV21 3AP
Tel: 01788 573241/560811

SPOD
(Association to aid the Sexual
  and Personal Relationships of
  People with a Disability)
286 Camden Road
London N7 OBJ
Tel: 0171 6078851

Talking Newspapers Association
  UK
National Recording Center
Heathfield
East Sussex TN21 8DB
Tel: 01435 866102

The Listening Library
12 Lant Street
London SE1 1QH
Tel: 0171 407 9417

Walsall Residential Home for
  People with Parkinson's
Mali Jenkins House
The Crescent
Walsall
West Midlands WS1 2BX
Enquiries and applications to:
Gill Howarth, Manager
Tel: 01922 746246

Index

217

Have you found **Parkinson's: a patient's view** practical and useful? If so, you may be interested in other books from Class Publishing.

Parkinson's at your fingertips
£11.95
Dr Marie Oxtoby and Professor Adrian Williams

Full of practical help and advice for people with Parkinson's disease and their families. This book gives you the information and the confidence to tackle the challenges that PD presents.

> 'Invaluable to everyone concerned with Parkinson's.'
> *Professor C D Marsden, Professor of Neurology, The National Hospital, London*

> 'A super DIY manual for patients and carers.'
> *Dr Bernard Dean*

Diabetes at your fingertips
THIRD EDITION £11.95
Professor Peter Sönksen,
Dr Charles Fox and Sister Sue Judd

461 questions on diabetes are answered clearly and accurately – the ideal reference book for everyone with diabetes.

> 'I will certainly recommend it to my patients ... I think it is brilliant.'
> *Robert Tattersall, Professor of Clinical Diabetes, Queen's Medical Centre, Nottingham*

High blood pressure at your fingertips £11.95
Dr Julian Tudor Hart

Dr Tudor Hart uses all his 26 years of experience as a General Practitioner and blood pressure expert to answer your questions on high blood pressure.

Cancer information at your fingertips
NEW SECOND EDITION
£11.95
Val Speechley and Maxine Rosenfield

Recommended by the Cancer Research Campaign, this book provides straightforward, practical and positive answers to all your questions about cancer.

Heart health at your fingertips
NEW! £11.95
Dr Graham Jackson

This invaluable handbook answers all your questions about your heart condition – and shows you how to lead a happy, healthy life.

Written by a leading cardiologist, the book gives practical advice on subjects ranging from diagnosis to treatment, and from diet to relationships.

Alzheimer's at your fingertips
NEW! £11.95
Harry Cayton, Dr Nori Graham, Dr James Warner

Clear and helpful answers to all your questions about Alzheimer's and other forms of dementia.

> 'An invaluable contribution to understanding all forms of dementia.'
> *Dr Jonathan Miller CBE, President of the Alzheimer's Disease Society*

Asthma at your fingertips
NEW SECOND EDITION
£11.95
Dr Mark Levy, Professor Sean Hilton and Greta Barnes MBE

This book shows you how to keep your asthma – or your family's asthma – under control, making it easier to live a full, happy and healthy life.

Allergies at your fingertips
NEW! £11.95
Dr Joanne Clough

At last – sensible, practical advice on allergies from an experienced medical expert.

'Extremely enjoyable and informative.'
Susan Ollier BSc, Scientific Director, British Allergy Foundation

PRIORITY ORDER FORM

Cut out or photocopy this form and send it (post free in the UK) to:

Class Publishing Priority Service
FREEPOST (no stamp needed)
LONDON W6 7BR

Tel: 01752 202301

Fax: 01752 202333

Please send me urgently
(tick boxes below)

Post included price per copy (UK only)

☐	**Parkinson's: a patient's view**	£17.95
☐	**Parkinson's at your fingertips**	£14.95
☐	**Diabetes at your fingertips**	£14.95
☐	**High blood pressure at your fingertips**	£14.95
☐	**Cancer information at your fingertips**	£14.95
☐	**Heart health at your fingertips**	£14.95
☐	**Alzheimer's at your fingertips**	£14.95
☐	**Asthma at your fingertips**	£14.95
☐	**Allergies at your fingertips**	£14.95

TOTAL: _____

Easy ways to pay
Cheque: I enclose a cheque payable to Class Publishing for
£_____
Credit card: please debit my   Access ☐ Visa ☐ Amex ☐
Switch ☐

Credit card number _____

Expiry date _____

Name _____

Address _____

_____

Town _____ County _____ Postcode _____

Daytime telephone number (in case of query) _____

Class Publishing's guarantee: remember that if, for any reason, you are not satisfied with these books, we will refund all your money, without any questions asked. Prices and VAT rates may be altered for reasons beyond our control.